Little Rock, late 1920s. Grandma Ida Potter holding unidentified baby, seated next to Anna Pauline "Billie" Potter Whitmore, who is holding the Ligons' daughter Mary. On far left is Cousin Helen Ligon Mashburn and her sister Wilma.

Torch Time Tales

Volume One

Torch Time Tales

Joni L. Whitmore

BEE PI Media

Volume One

Published by: BEE PI Media

Hardcover ISBN: 979-8-9862045-0-5
Paperback ISBN: 979-8-9862045-1-2
Ebook ISBN: 979-8-9862045-1-2
Audiobook ISBN: 979-8-9862045-3-6

First Edition
First Printing June 2022

Cover Photo credit: Patrick M. Whitmore

Contact information for distribution and reprint rights:
Torchtimetales.org

Back Cover Photo

WJW and Eloise Winn Whitmore, after eloping, return to Oregon to meet the in-laws. Front Row: WJW, Erma Rickard Winn, John Winn. Back row: EWW, her brother James "Jim" Winn, and her sister Maxine Winn.

To My Teachers

Table of Contents

Author's Note

First things first. I am nearing the end of my days. A while back, I was given two months to two years to live. I have what's called a broken heart in more ways than one. That will have to wait. My window in life is coming and going before my eyes, and there's something that can't wait any longer.

I have a responsibility and an offering to you, which, until now, has been left unaddressed. I am, through these volumes, leaving you with my most intimate, invaluable possession: the elements of my spiritual estate. I hope I get this completed before I depart.

My aim is for this offering to allow the illuminations that have appeared through the cracks between the worlds that I have experienced to continue to expand in strength within you. That light and those illuminations are my spiritual estate, wonder-filled gifts that keep on giving. I'm counting on it. If I were unable or unwilling to pass the torch, the light and wisdom might pass with me as I go.

In this spiritual and ancestral memoir, with the direct intervention of several of my nephews and two cousins, you will accompany us through intersections of the past, present, and future that bring us full circle to this point. My life serves as an educational vehicle to help ease your own path toward self-realization and enlightenment. The history of my extended family, with all our scandals over twelve hundred years, reveals where we've gotten stuck or lost our way with one another the world around.

Your own senses will gauge the truths to be gleaned for yourself. You don't have to take my word for any of it. Science now confirms we inherit much of who we are from our ancestors and that much of the known universe is probably conscious. My ancestors don't explain all of who I am, although their histories have resolved many of the mysteries. I am a freak in my family, as you'll come to understand, and a seemingly unlikely candidate for this effort. And therein lies the grist for the mill of improving functionality, capacity, and potentiality for all of us human beings. If I can do it, every one of us can.

With infinite help from those here and beyond, I am convinced beyond a shadow of a doubt that breakthroughs in human understanding are pathways to self-realization. As these tales wind back and forth in space and time, your own reality may very well begin to improve in unanticipated, positive ways. It will be noticeable. That impact and benefit will multiply over time. It is meant to be for each of us.

I have come to understand and acknowledge my family history – for better and for worse. As a consequence of that understanding, I am making amends accordingly. I was literally summoned here to help. That historical family fact has been plainly staring me in the face throughout my life. With help from every direction, I'm coming to terms with my own spiritual responsibilities for what I've been bequeathed. Now beyond my mature years, I'm just learning it was written in the stars all along.

Tongue in cheek, you might say I'm a sort of grease monkey for a wheel that was predicted to arrive right about now more than twenty-five hundred years ago. It is foretold to be a golden era of human and spiritual rejuvenation that directly follows one in which we've been lost for some time, adrift in a sea of corruption.

It was also foretold what a difficult journey it is for those who attempt to communicate all of this, and I ask for your patience and assistance. Importantly, benefits multiply – each individual, out to even the fiftieth person who comes in contact with that first one who has a spiritual breakthrough in human understanding and then further shares the light will all accrue benefits to the mind and other senses through engagement with others.

It is my intention to help you and our world of relations move to a profoundly improved frame of mind and an enhanced reality of calm and clarity. The amount of change you achieve is up to you. We are each our own self-limiting factor. As each of us is in a different place when approaching this point, your ability to absorb it and your reactions to it will differ. Importantly, the more movement each and every one of us is able to make over time, the easier it will be for everyone now and in the future.

These efforts are meant to serve as a contribution to the revival of a meaningful roadmap for the mind for the greater good. The greater our awareness, the stronger our attention and the more strength we'll have to maintain and facilitate our connections to our higher selves, one another, and our purpose here on earth and beyond.

Yes, we are all connected. Yes, we are all related. And yes, indeed, we appear to share an infinite mind. Did I mention the universe is interactive? Wonders never cease!

Buddha said that to know enlightenment, one must know ignorance. Eventually, he reminds us, everyone makes their way into enlightenment: all of the women and even the worst of the men eventually go. And we each have the capacity to find our own spiritual path, if necessary. However, he cautions we may climb steep steps when great vehicles exist to help along the way.

Imagine that!

See the light, be the light, and remember to pass the torch before you go!

CHAPTER 1

The Tathagata

"*What repeats through time?* You have to admit it's a simple question," I began to explain to the family and friends who'd gathered to hear the latest edition of my aunt Joni's *Torch Time Tales*. Privately speaking, I considered myself an unlikely candidate for the job from the get-go, but the responsibility had fallen squarely in my lap, whether I liked it or not.

"We all receive the same handwritten question when it's our time, sent on a plain white postcard," I continued. "It arrived in my case sometime shortly after one of my birthdays as a younger adult. That question was the only thing on it. It wasn't even signed, but I recognized my aunt's handwriting. The postcard was unmistakably her work." I took a moment to look around at the expressions on the faces of those comfortably assembled.

"I have to confess to you I've never been fond of riddles and found myself frustrated that the answer wasn't coming to me. I think I

tossed it in a pile of junk and didn't think more about it that day."
I paused. "Funny thing is, I really was fascinated by the question.
The harder I tried not to think about it, the more it seemed to bug
me. Anyway, a few weeks passed before the next card arrived. This
one really made me sit up and take notice."

I read to them from one of the cards that had been sent to me
long ago:

> *If and when the previously posted question is answered, the*
> *bearer of this card, as a descendant of those generations so in-*
> *volved, will have been determined self-eligible and shall, if*
> *they choose to participate, be summoned to the continuation of*
> Torch Time Tales *at a place and time to be determined. This*
> *is a time-limited offer. No cash value. Not good with other of-*
> *fers.*

"This one got my attention," I said firmly as I passed it around for
the group to inspect. "I remember thinking I had no idea what
this was all about, and I wasn't sure I wanted to play. It had to be a
setup! I half suspected my parents had colluded with my aunt – on
what and why, I wasn't sure. Obviously, that line of thinking made
me very uneasy at the time."

A few of the seniors laughed, appreciating my youthful
predicament.

"Ironically, what I eventually learned would rock my world. And
now that you're all here, I can finally tell you – I was never the same
afterward. In short, we share one outrageous past, you and I, like it
or not," I added sheepishly and noticed an eyebrow or two begin
to rise.

"And now, in what seems a blink of an eye, I'm an old man," I
relayed with chagrin to chuckles from the group, "reigniting *Torch*

Time Tales with you all in the hot seat I once owned. This tradition is set to start again and, with any luck, will replace the worn wheels our family's been spinning on far too long."

I paused for a moment before continuing in a near whisper. "My aunt Joni is reminding me that a Tathagata, an ancient Sanskrit word, is one who has thus come to declare the truth and one who has thus gone. The truth, as it turns out, is stranger than fiction. And it has a habit of repeating itself. It took me a while, but I finally got it. Funny thing is, it dawned on me one day while I wasn't thinking about anything at all."

CHAPTER 2

The Invitation

By the time I got going on my aunt's invitation, I was well more than legally an adult. My girlfriend had ditched me for someone else, leaving me an emotional mess. My older brother had suggested that a trip to see Aunt Joni might be the therapeutic ticket I needed. I'd just come off a nearly twenty-hour stint between work and making the long haul driving down to California to see her and was beyond tired. I'd never been up so long with so little sleep. In hindsight, I have to say all of it left me at a disadvantage with her from the start.

"How do these tales begin?" I asked her that night shortly after my arrival.

"They don't have a beginning," Aunt Joni answered pointedly, "and they don't have an end."

"I don't get it!"

"I don't, either, and I don't know the whole story. I'm just your torchbearer. However, I can tell you I'm ecstatic to see you right here and now!"

"What do you mean?" I pressed rudely. "What kind of story doesn't have a beginning and an end?"

My aunt gave me the hairy eyeball, and I began to get an uneasy feeling in the pit of my gut. It had been a really long day. It hit me then with full force that this visit with my aunt wasn't necessarily going to be a walk in the park.

"So, how do you start a tale that doesn't have a beginning?" I finally asked when it became painfully clear she wasn't going to respond to my initial line of questioning.

"That's a very good question!" she answered excitedly. "Your father warned me you had grown up to be quite a cracker-jack. I'm delighted to see it! It will make my job easier."

"What job is that?" I asked, still shocked by her quick turnaround.

"Before our time together has come and gone, I must pass you the torch! No small task," my aunt replied half to herself, staring into space. "If I drop it, I'll have failed myself, you, and possibly an infinite list of future generations," she added with a tone and expression that suggested she was serious or half in the bag – I wasn't sure which.

I felt my eyebrows furrow as it dawned on me with even greater alarm that there was something significant expected of me in all of this. "Let me get this straight," I said, cutting to the chase. "It's your job to tell me a tale that has no beginning and no end? Is this just another riddle?" I could feel my frustration again beginning to rise.

"In hindsight, it may be the most important job in my life," she said with a large sigh. "And there are an awful lot of riddles in this tale, no doubt about it." She chuckled. "But that should make the telling, and hopefully, the listening, that much more enjoyable!"

I was speechless. There was nothing to do but wait. I yawned and stretched my arms back over my head to get some oxygen flowing to my very confused brain. My face must have reflected my exasperation.

"I can see that we've done enough for one night," she said, slowly rising from her chair.

"What do you mean? We haven't even gotten started, and you don't even seem to know how to begin!" I said before I could stop the ugly words from spilling out of my mouth.

She stared at me for what seemed an eternity. "You've traveled a long way and are clearly very tired. You've heard Rome wasn't built in a day?"

I nodded, feeling patronized.

"Hopefully, we'll have enough time to undertake this part of the effort!"

Those words, her last of the day, left me wondering about all of it.

* * *

The sun dropped quickly on the next day – my first full day there with her. I'd slept late, still exhausted from the trip down, and had woken half in a fog. I was finally starting to come around with the help of some coffee when my aunt whisked me off on her golf cart.

She was attempting to explain to me that the Hidden Valley Lake community had just celebrated its fiftieth anniversary. A crew of retiring Boise Cascade employees had grown sweet on the place while logging the enormous oaks and had secured a bunch of the property from the company after they finished. Evidently, they drafted a long-range community development plan and eventually engaged golf course design legend Billy Bell to help them construct a championship golf course as the centerpiece for their vacation and retirement home dreams.

We spent the day seeing the local sights. The view from the top of the fifteenth tee, not far from her house, was a wowza – with a breathtaking panorama of Coyote Valley and Mt. Saint Helena. What a way to wake up, I thought to myself, delighted to be there, taking in the sunshine. I imagined hitting a two-hundred-yard drive off the side of the mountain and easily making the fairway down below. But I hadn't seen my aunt for some years, and we had quite a bit of catching up to do that afternoon.

Eventually, we settled on one of the patio couches underneath the veranda in the backyard. When I first stepped outside, I was taken aback. It was almost more than my eyes could take in. I hadn't expected the natural beauty of the view, with some of the largest oaks I'd ever seen about a hundred yards or so to the south and a good-sized pond in between. The enormous oaks formed a line that ran parallel to the pond, both of which ran perpendicular to the eighteenth fairway on the golf course. I spied a mature egret wading behind a group of ducklings, snapping up fish fry they sent in its direction.

My older brother had clued me in to the fact that Lake County had some of the cleanest air in California. Given my cynical nature, I had a hard time imagining I would be able to discern any difference. Yet it was impossible to miss, as the fresh air made my lungs want to breathe. It was as if the air were naturally sweetened.

I felt the first of multiple waves of relaxation course through me as I allowed myself to finally begin to unwind. I have to say, there was something extraordinary about being there, but I couldn't quite put my finger on it. I was gazing at the colorful layers of the Mayacamas Mountains, which wrapped the southern and western sides of the community, when, all of a sudden, out of the corner of my eye, I caught sight of a blur of green and hot pink as it flashed close by us before landing on one of the two enormous palms in the center of the backyard.

"What was that?" I asked delightedly.

"Have you ever had the pleasure of meeting a hummingbird before?" my aunt asked me.

"Was that really a hummingbird?" I asked with amazement, and before she had an opportunity to respond, I added, "No, I haven't ever seen one up close and personal before. This is a first for me. Do they always fly so close?"

Again, before my aunt could respond, the same tiny little bird flew right up in front of my face. It hovered there briefly before returning to one of the amazing golden yellow flowers shaded between the palms. "Wow! That's just way cool."

My aunt laughed happily at my delight. "They are very sociable creatures. You are a new face to them here today. Your arrival has been noticed and acknowledged, I'd say."

Something inside of me stirred at that moment. I could swear I had a fleeting feeling of joy.

* * *

That evening after dinner, we sat down on the bench outside. Without lights from the city to interfere, the stars shone against the backdrop of the night sky more brightly than I'd ever seen before. I could make out constellations I'd seen on star charts but never with my own eyes. The ones I did recognize seemed upside down. There was quite a bit in my aunt's world that way. I couldn't guess what she'd say next.

"I've got another question for you," Aunt Joni began.

"Uh-oh. Is this another tough one?" I asked, already finding myself wondering how long it would take me to figure it out.

She didn't bite about the level of difficulty. However, just like the last question, this one would also catch me out in left field.

"Like the first one, this one also dates back to what we'd consider ancient history. Who do you know that lived twenty-five hundred years ago who understood the world is infinite?"

"When?" I replied, completely stunned by her off-the-wall question.

"Call it 565 to 486 BC," she responded without hesitation.

"Geez, Aunt Joni, my brother warned me that some of your questions were tough, but man, oh, man. I'm going to have to sit with that one."

"No problem. No rush. In the scope of history, this question deserves some fair consideration."

"Thanks. That helps a lot," I added sarcastically. "Can you proceed without having an answer from me on that one?" I asked her sheepishly, sitting with the notion that there was someone out there in history I'd missed who understood the world was infinite while everyone else was still debating whether or not it was flat. How could I have missed that?

"You may also be unaware that many families around the world have carried the belief through time that the actions we take in our lives may influence or directly impact future generations," she said. "When I became aware of this idea, I couldn't grasp it, either. It seemed unlikely to be true. I didn't know much of anything about the generations before my own. How could they possibly influence me?"

"That's a fascinating question." I began to contemplate the idea that my ancestors were somehow influencing me from beyond the grave. It seemed highly unlikely to me. "So, what do you think now?"

"For now, I say we go back just six or seven generations from your own and see what we can for ourselves. Perhaps the tales will speak for themselves."

"Can we really do that?" I asked, skeptical, to say the least.

"As a matter of fact, we can, and if we have time, you and I might be able to go way back. But first off, let's figure out who I'm talking about here, shall we?"

I nodded, but I wasn't going to be much help.

"For now, our tale will start with your father's father's father's father's father's father, your great-great-great-great-grandfather."

"How long ago did he live?" I asked as my eyebrows furrowed.

"Not that long ago," she replied innocently, "but more than a couple of hundred years ago."

"You're shittin' me!" I exclaimed before I could catch myself. "More than two hundred years ago?" My face scrunched up in disbelief.

My aunt nodded. "It's a great time to begin, although it doesn't matter where we start in the scheme of things."

"Huh?" I mustered, confused by her answer. She refused to take the hint.

"Our long-departed relation just so happens to share his birth year with the United States of America! The Continental Congress held authority until March 4, 1789, when the United States Constitution was ratified. George Washington was elected the first president on April 30."

"That at least gives me some perspective on his timeframe in history," I replied.

"That same year," she went on, "and just around the corner from all that excitement, Burwell Temple Whitmore was born in Dinwiddie County, Virginia. He is your great-great-great-great-grandfather. Burwell was raised about thirty miles south of

Richmond. Believe it or not, Virginia had more than a half-million people by then and was growing fast."

"How many greats was that again?" I asked, still trying to get it straight in my head.

My aunt began counting back the relations from my father on the fingers of her left hand. "I count four greats. Six generations prior to your own. Same difference if you start with Burwell and count forward. You are the sixth generation beyond Burwell's."

"Wait another minute. Virginia already had a half-million people by 1789? I had no idea!"

My aunt nodded and smiled wryly. "Burwell was eight years old when John Adams succeeded George Washington to become the second president of the United States. However, our Virginia boy Burwell largely grew up under Thomas Jefferson's span in office. Virginia had over eight hundred thousand people by the year 1800, believe it or not. From that point in time, it took two hundred more years for Virginia to grow another tenfold in size. By 2011, Virginia had more than eight million!" Aunt Joni added, appearing to get sidetracked.

"And?" I prompted when she didn't continue immediately.

"Anyway, the first twenty years of Burwell's life spanned the first four American presidents. James Madison, our fourth president, was sworn in 1809, the year Burwell turned twenty years old. What an interesting time to be alive," she mused. "Burwell married Amanda Elder Whitmore, your great-great-great-great-grandmother, and the pair had a large family."

I took a sip of the ice water I'd brought outside. The moment she paused, I found my mind doing the math. She'd actually started well more than 230 years ago. My older brother, who had already run this gauntlet with my aunt when he'd begun the lengthy process of scanning our ancestral family photos, had cautioned me to stay on my toes and really try to hear her on as many levels as I could. I hadn't really understood what he'd meant at the time, but I was beginning to get the idea that there was more to this than I could fathom.

"Their third child, Richard Augustus Whitmore, is your great-great-great-grandfather. He was also born in Dinwiddie County, Virginia, in 1823, toward the end of President Monroe's term. President number five," she added before I had a chance to ask. "Richard would have been a toddler in 1825, the year President John Quincy Adams's service began."

"The presidents didn't last very long," I observed, a bit surprised.

"There was quite a bit of turnover in the early days of government as America learned to find her feet," she agreed. "Andrew Jackson, our seventh president, was sworn in in the spring of 1829. Jackson was a piece of work. He advocated for limited government, individual liberties, and democracy while supporting the continuation of slavery and forcing the dislocation of thousands of Native Americans from five tribes in the southeastern part of the country to what would eventually become Oklahoma."

"He sounds like a piece of work! That's awful." It was fair to say my own views on politics were still evolving at that point in my life. So much of it seemed like power-grabbing horseshit. "And Burwell's family, were they still in Virginia at that point?"

"Yep, Burwell and his family were still in Virginia when Jackson was elected. They moved the next year, in 1830. As I recall, the US Congress passed the Indian Removal Act that year, which may have had something to do with Burwell's decision to leave Virginia and head for Tennessee."

"Why do you say that?"

"When the government began forcing Native Americans to give up their lands, the 'pioneers,' as they were called historically, jumped on the opportunity to move westward as large areas of acreage were made available."

"That's just so ugly," I responded, watching my aunt's face as she grimaced and nodded.

"Richard was still a young lad, all of about seven years old, when Burwell and Amanda decided to attempt the move. They joined a wagon train with five other pioneering Virginian families headed for the wilderness of western Tennessee. It was a six-hundred-mile trip to get there. That would have been an adventure of a lifetime for a boy his age."

"Wow! How long did it take them to make a six-hundred-mile trip in a wagon train?"

"I wondered about that myself. Wagon train speeds varied with the passengers; estimates range from one to four miles per hour, depending on the route and the age of the travelers. Those walking with toddlers might have made a mile an hour. Top estimates put the average daily distance traveled at, say, ten to fifteen miles a day. Given only those variables, my guess is that it may have taken them the better part of six weeks to two months."

"That's quite a trip," I responded as I shook my head in amazement at the idea.

"According to historical accounts, they followed the Natchez Trace from Nashville and then traveled on to Mississippi, where they regrouped for provisions before moving north into Hardeman County, Tennessee. Richard was raised on a large plantation in the southwestern corner, in a spot they called Grand Junction. From what I've gathered, the family prospered."

"That wagon train trip had to have opened his eyes a little," I couldn't help remarking.

"Yes, I suspect it did," she responded. "There were seven children born in Richard's family, and while he wasn't the oldest child – he had two older sisters – he was the oldest son. In those days, there were different expectations for the sons. They often shouldered a greater responsibility level in the family. In many places, they still do," she added, looking straight at me.

Believe you me, I tried like hell not to take that comment personally. Thankfully, my dear aunt picked up where she'd left off, letting me off the hook for the moment, anyway.

"Given the success of the Whitmore plantation, however, Richard never wanted for something to eat, never wanted for clothes, boots, or books. Sure, he worked hard – harder than you could possibly imagine. And yet he had everything a young man of that age could want and then some!" My aunt shifted around on the bench before continuing.

I found myself remembering my father sharing how hard they'd all worked as kids growing up. Times had certainly changed over the centuries. I was sure I'd never had to work anywhere near that hard as a child. My aunt interrupted my musing.

"The two Whitmore girls aimed to become teachers, a respectable position for women in those days. Their younger brother, Richard, was their chief guinea pig. As a result of their efforts, Richard could read, write, add, subtract, and multiply before he entered elementary school. What an enormous gift they gave him!"

"That's impressive!"

"Richard's oldest sister, Sallie, was their ringleader," she went on. "She was two years older than her sister, Elizabeth, and five ahead of Richard. Sallie had experienced the benefits and drawbacks of numerous teachers and their methods, growing up as she did in Virginia. She was smart enough to understand that when she was having fun, learning came easily, and time flew by. When a teacher was stern or dull, she found herself struggling to grasp the significance of what they were trying to convey. They made it twice as difficult as it needed to be!"

"I had a few super teachers," I replied, nodding in agreement. "They really did make it easier to learn."

"Sallie had a talent for finding fun ways to share what she was learning with her growing brood of siblings, and the bunch of them got along famously. They were very close! That is, until she died suddenly at the age of twelve," she concluded abruptly.

"She was twelve years old?" I asked, surprised by this turn of events.

"Yep," Aunt Joni answered. "Twelve years old. Not a very long ride and yet not insignificant in the scheme of things. Richard was only seven years old at the time. Her passing struck him hard. He counted on her being older and wiser – to settle the disputes that arose among them with an even and fair hand and to help them see goodness in people and in one another. They had such fun together! For Richard, his sister Sallie's death seemed to leave a gaping hole in what had been their family dynamic."

"That's kind of sad," I said softly.

"It was a tough year all around. Richard's mother, Amanda Elder Whitmore, was not herself. Depression at the death of her firstborn made it difficult for her to engage in their family life. However difficult it had to be for them all, to complicate matters emotionally, Burwell and Amanda were preparing for the coming of their sixth child."

With one look, my aunt knew I had no words to respond. All I could do was shake my head in amazement.

"Burwell hoped the newborn would rekindle Amanda's love of life – and perhaps it did. She gave birth to a baby girl. He insisted they name her Amanda, hoping her namesake would give his wife reason to go on." Aunt Joni paused to take a drink.

"What do you mean?"

"Remember, Burwell and Amanda had just buried their oldest daughter, and add to that a newborn and the possibility she may have been experiencing postpartum depression. Richard spent months watching his mother withdraw. His father also made himself scarce, finding every last thing that needed tending to somewhere else."

"Oh. Okay, I'm getting it," I said when she paused.

"With his beloved sister gone and his parents seemingly missing in action, Richard doubled his efforts to pick up where Sallie had left off with their lessons. Learning would become one of the most cherished habits of Richard's life."

"Wow. It had to have really hit him," I replied. "As much as we've tangled during our growing-up years, I can't imagine losing my brother."

"Richard had to focus his attention on something to get through it. So, early every morning and late into the night, he read everything he could find – in his free time, that is, free from the drudgery of working the plantation. And he took up carving, which calmed him and gave him something else to focus on. I suspect he liked watching the tiny changes made to the wood with each stroke of his blade eventually amount to something."

"That's cool. I've never really had a chance to try carving. So, what happened next?" I asked, now curious about his fate.

"Time marched on, with each day's routine looking much the same. Burwell, meanwhile, began to amass property in earnest. In January of 1836, he bought 381 acres bordering their original homestead to the south and east."

She paused to take a sip of her beverage. "Burwell's wife, Amanda, carried her seventh child that year, when Richard turned thirteen."

"That's a lot more land, and this was their last child?" I wanted to be sure I was tracking.

"Yep, Richard and his older sister, Elizabeth, grew up quickly, charged by their father to assume more responsibility for their younger brothers, John and George. Their mother had her hands full with her newborn daughter, Martha Virginia Whitmore, named after Burwell's mother and their state of birth. It was a turning point into adulthood for Richard, foreshadowing the increased responsibility he would assume in the family for years to come."

"What do you mean by that?"

"Burwell was losing himself in his growing empire," she responded. "In the spring of 1837, Martin Van Buren was elected the country's eighth president. Meanwhile, Burwell bought another ninety acres to the north and east of the acreage he'd purchased the year before. The year after that, he bought another one hundred eighty acres to the north and west."

"Wow! That's a lot of land. How did they work it all?" I asked innocently.

"If a property owner held slaves, ownership was transferred with the sale of the property as part of the negotiated price. I'm sorry to have to tell you that Burwell owned many people before he was through," she responded bluntly.

"Oh, my God. I had no idea! Are you messing with me?"

My aunt looked over at me and slowly shook her head. My eyebrows were raised in disbelief, but no more words came out of my mouth. She took that as a sign to continue.

"Remember my mentioning the Indian Removal Act of 1830?" she asked me.

I nodded, still too stunned to speak.

"By 1838, the Cherokees had been assembled by the military in their remaining capital in eastern Tennessee. The military had orders to march them westward all the way out to Oklahoma. They could have walked near Grand Junction, not far from Burwell

Whitmore's plantation. If you think about it, prior to the 1830 act of Congress, all of the lands Burwell purchased would have originally been occupied by Cherokee people and other Native American tribes."

"God, that's really awful. Do you suppose Richard witnessed what happened?"

"It would have been hard to miss! They certainly would have known about it, with thousands of people and a bunch of soldiers on the move. He would have been about fifteen when that horrific march took place. If that wasn't enough, he was also a daily witness to his own father's actions."

"Huh?" I responded, afraid I had missed something in the translation.

"Burwell now ruled his roost with an ever-tighter iron fist. He had become a mean, ornery son of a gun. It was questionable which folks feared more, his words or his whipping post. Yet it wasn't enough. He became relentless, pushing everyone to the breaking point. And he plowed his profits into buying more land."

"Sounds like a friendly kind of guy," I threw in sarcastically.

"Burwell argued with Richard every day, trying to talk him out of his latest plans to escape the family business. From the father's perspective, Richard was the first male child – destined, if you will, to take over the plantation. But for Richard, it was hard to explain to his father why he could not, why he would not stay. He flashed to some of his earliest memories with his sisters playing school. Thanks to them, he'd been introduced to a different track and many other fields, whole worlds full of knowledge." She shook her head.

"Maybe his saving grace," I offered.

"Maybe," she agreed. "Over the next four years, America had her own difficulties and would turn the leadership mantle over several more times. Our ninth president, William Harrison, had been a military man. At the time, he was famous for leading offensives against Native Americans. Harrison served one month and then died of pneumonia. John Tyler, our tenth president, was followed by James Polk, sworn in in the spring of 1845."

"Those aren't presidents we learn much about. I can't even imagine the presidential politics of those days," I commented wryly. "So, what happened with Burwell and Richard?"

"By 1847, Burwell had acquired two more properties north of his own, a 144-acre tract that summer and twenty-nine acres that fall. His plantation was now massive in size and took all his effort. His slaves, sons, and family were cut no slack. According to one of the cultural resource managers of the Ames Plantation, which stores and studies the history of that part of Tennessee, Burwell was at that point one of the largest commercial agricultural producers in Hardeman County, and evidently, he was also doing some fancy footwork to stay ahead of the tax collectors."

"Huh? What do you mean?" I couldn't help asking. This was new territory for yours truly.

"The historical records were revealing. Every year, there were separate entries maintained in different community ledgers that tracked what was going on. They noted landowners and their families, total acreage and numbers of slaves owned, land purchased and sold, as well as agricultural production detailed by crop."

"Why'd they do that?" I asked, not clear where she was going with all of this.

"It provided a summary for the tax collectors to make their assessments, which the landowners were responsible for paying toward their share of the county expenses and upkeep. Later on, the census and tax records were compared. The historical records provided to me by the Ames Plantation reveal Burwell grossly underreported his acreage and slaves every year for more than three decades!"

I about choked on my sip of water at that news. "He wasn't honest?" I managed to get out after swallowing. I had to put the question to her to hear how she might respond.

"It doesn't appear so. However, it's possible he didn't keep track of or remember exactly what he'd told them from one year to the next. Men drank a lot in those days. By some accounts, from the 1830s and beyond, American men were consuming on average seven bottles of hard liquor every month, not quite two bottles a week. That's enough to stunt anybody's memory!"

"Wow!" I couldn't help exclaiming. I'd done my share of partying, but that much hard liquor would have left the toughest of us on the floor.

"According to the slave census, there were many years in which Burwell reported barely half the actual number of enslaved people working his plantation!"

"That's just incredible. I had no idea. I studied slavery, but I never suspected our family held slaves," I said, still shell-shocked by what I was hearing.

"I know how you feel. I could hardly believe it myself when I first learned." She let out a long sigh, which I couldn't help but echo.

"Wow," was about all I could muster as the full weight of the knowledge confronted me.

"The census revealed his name was spelled inconsistently over the years; he was listed as Burwell, Burrell, and some years as Berle. The Ames Plantation staff assured me those records were for the same properties owned by the same man. It's possible he went by all three names. Some relations have suggested he may have taken on a shortened version of Burwell when they moved from Virginia."

My aunt paused for a moment. "To give you a sense of the scope of his operation, when it finally sold, Burwell Whitmore's plantation encompassed more than eight hundred and twenty-four acres."

"It's almost unbelievable," I answered her. "I can see how families would want to bury this kind of ancestral history!"

"Like it or not, that's the legacy Burwell and most, but thankfully not all, of the founding fathers left for us," she acknowledged. "It's up to us to determine what we do with this living awareness. Without it, we unknowingly stand on the backs of our dead as we try pushing ahead in life, leaving behind unresolved issues from our collective past that weigh us all down."

I heard the echo of her words inside my head as I stared out toward the horizon. Neither one of us spoke for a few moments before she continued.

"Our nation was designed for its survival. Incremental change with checks and balances was meant to ensure the stability of a fragile, young government – and in the process, it froze in time for centuries the advantages all of those religious, political, economic, and family power structures maintained at the expense of others. The power and wealth they enjoy as a result of holding that upper hand over everyone else for so long reached new extremes in the twenty-first century."

"It certainly gives me a different picture of my life through the lens of my ancestors!" It was difficult for me to admit it, but it was true.

"When the truth about Burwell finally pierced through to the surface in my own life, I looked to the historical context of the time to better understand him," my aunt went on. "Truly, Burwell would have been considered small potatoes in comparison to the ultra-wealthy of that era. Yet there it was – he was part of a small handful of wealthy families who would ultimately help ensure the continuation of privilege at the expense of most everyone else for hundreds of years to come." She shook her head.

"I really didn't have a clue our family was part of all that!" I finally blurted out.

"By the way," Aunt Joni continued, "if you're ever back in that neck of the woods, you'll find Burwell's plantation intact. And I have to say, having been there, it's like walking back into history. Very little has changed there since the days of his rule."

"Really?" I asked her skeptically. "How is that possible?"

"The entire estate was purchased by the Ames Plantation, I think I mentioned. It has multi-prong educational and scientific missions, established by the Ames family to benefit the University of Tennessee, and is the largest land-resource research facility in the state. It's probably best known for being home to the National Field Trial Championship, a competition for hunting dogs. The foundation that's involved has kept the historical records and tracked the original families and their descendants. In that role, they eventually ended up with some of the Whitmore family records when they purchased Burwell's estate. We have them to thank for their help."

She slowly rose from the bench. "This is a good spot to wrap up for the night."

"All right, if you insist!" I declared emphatically.

CHAPTER 3

Venturing beyond the Known

I woke up to another beautiful day in California without a cloud in the sky. I found my way out to the kitchen to find Aunt Joni had already been up for hours. We shared snippets of news over breakfast. Forecasters were calling for the possibility of rain in the next day or two. Although the long drought had ended, Californians still seemed to appreciate the rain and even the clouds in a way that surprised me, having been socked in and drenched most of my life in the Pacific Northwest.

My aunt declared it was a good day for us to be outside while the weather was still cooperating. She had offered me some work while I was there for the month, and I'd readily accepted. I wasn't quite sure what it might amount to, but I was game anyway.

As we walked slowly around the outside of the house, she pointed out several possible projects. We soon settled on our targets for the day and went to work. Four large sycamore trees lined the easement with the neighbor next door to the east. The limbs hadn't been trimmed back in a while and were attempting to merge with the Chinese wisteria over the pergola.

I chose the extension trimmer and began dropping sycamore branches hanging over from the yard next door more than twenty feet to the ground. It was easy and reasonably fun. Within about fifteen minutes, I'd created a fairly good-size pile. Joni worked the six grapevines, trimming leaves and cane on the other side of the yard. When we were done with the sorting, we had several large buckets of sycamore and grape leaves for the compost.

After lunch, we hit the links. My dad had been a landscape architect and designed several golf courses in Oregon and Washington during his career. He loved the game, as had my grandparents. My brother and I had both started golfing young, but neither one of us had the time to get out anymore. Joni had also learned to play in elementary school but had largely let it go until after she'd retired. She called the pro shop that morning and had us checked in to tee off first thing that afternoon. We would be at the tee, hitting our first drives, not even ten minutes later.

As we approached the community restaurant and pro shop, I asked Joni how her golf cart, "Mary," got her name.

"She's named in honor of the original owner, may she rest in peace. You'll see."

The last part didn't make sense to me, but I let it go. As we pulled up to the first tee, Joni pointed out a bronze plaque beside us on a large rock. The plaque resolved the "Mary" mystery pretty quickly. "Mary" had been a longtime course champion, and the plaque acknowledged her as "our inspiration to golf."

"That's way cool," I offered.

I was a little antsy as I got out of the cart. I hadn't golfed in a while and began having a reality check with myself about my golf capabilities. My aunt had assured me that we could expect to have the course largely to ourselves on weekday afternoons. That reflection helped calm me down quite a bit.

I will confess it took me a while before I was able to get my drives to go where I thought I was aiming. It really did help not to have anyone coming up behind us. I could take my time, get prepared for my shot, and give it a good stroke. All said and done, golfing with Aunt Joni was hilarious. I hadn't laughed so hard in a while. It was amazing to have so much fun while golfing downright miserably. The game is deceiving that way. It's really much harder than it looks, except for when it's not. And it's more fun than it looks as well, again, except for when it's not.

That afternoon, I confirmed for myself that my aunt was just about an ace putter. She shared with me that her economics advisor in college, a professor by the name of "Chip" Case, who had some kind of housing index named after him – I forget the name – had calculated putting was at least thirty percent of a golf round. According to the family, my aunt's putting skills had been learned from my departed grandmother Eloise. I couldn't figure out how she did it. But before we were done for the day, she clued me in on how to use my peripheral vision to spy the flag pin while keeping my head and eyes zeroed in on the ball below. Now there was a priceless tip! I saw an immediate improvement in my game. I have to say, my aunt continued to surprise me.

* * *

"I threw you off course last night with my question about Burwell's plantation," I offered as we sat down outside early that evening after showering and having a bite to eat.

"Thank you for the reminder! That gives me the clue I needed to recommence. Let's just say that after witnessing the misery his father, Burwell, put everyone through, Richard must have developed very different ideas about his own destiny. Each passing day, the yoke of it all cut into him more deeply than the next – until he could not stand it anymore."

"What happened to Richard?" I asked her.

"I'm not sure what the last straw was for Richard. I can tell you that by 1849, the mantle passed nationally from President Polk to the twelfth president, Zachary Taylor," she said, looking directly into my eyes.

I thought about my own attempts to leave home. Both my brother and I had moved in and out of our dad's house a few times over the year after our parents divorced.

"I suspect that from Richard's perspective, at twenty-six, it was clear to him that if he didn't set out on his own, he never would. He was surrounded by folks who'd spent most of their lives there and were unlikely to leave. Life expectancy during those days was all of thirty-five."

"Wow. What a trip! That's not very long."

"Many stayed where they were out of fear of the unknowns of a new location and any hope of a new vocation. Why fritter life away trying something new someplace else that might not work out, especially when one considered the potential dangers lurking around every corner? His brothers, John and George, were of that mind – the plantation provided them with more than enough, and he expected they would spend their lives there with their families – if they were fortunate enough to find women who'd have them."

She paused for a few moments before going on with the story. I stayed quiet.

"But for Richard, to stay in Tennessee and continue on with his father would have been a form of death," she explained. "His spirit was restless – and he wanted a life of his own. He'd read enough to know there was a huge world to discover. Once he'd made up his mind and gathered his resources, Richard took off."

"Where did he go?" I couldn't help asking.

"Leaders of those days spread visions of their manifest destiny, a term coined by a journalist to describe the phenomenon of generations of immigrants pushing onward and outward to the West Coast. The population on the East Coast continued to swell, and the move westward was the escape valve. People latched on to the idea of manifest destiny – that the Europeans of America were destined by God to settle North America all the way to the Pacific Ocean. I would venture that many of these pseudo-civilized white folks of the time perceived the western regions of the country to be largely untamed and quite dangerous. But Richard finally had the wherewithal, smarts, and nerve to board a ship to take him out to California via the horn of South America, avoiding the dangers involved in traveling over land."

"I didn't know people were using boats to get out to California in those days," I replied, imagining myself hanging off a ship rail while cruising down the coastline of South America.

"Like so many, Richard may have caught the gold-rush fever and aimed to take part in the action directly. It was a tumultuous time. President Taylor lasted a little more than a year in office. Millard Fillmore was elected the thirteenth president in 1850."

"But what happened to Richard?" I asked her. "Did he strike it rich in California?"

"Life on his own may not have been the ideal he dreamed," she answered. "Evidently, the gold rush didn't pan out for him. Within two years of leaving for his adventure west, he was back to square one at home again in Tennessee."

"You're kidding. Just like that? He made a round trip out to California and then back to Tennessee in two years? For those days, that guy had to be moving!" I exclaimed.

Aunt Joni laughed at my fun. "That was 1851. At the ripe old age of twenty-eight, he returned and married your great-great-great-grandmother Cornelia Ann Brown, who was then nineteen years old. To make sure his father couldn't get his hooks back into him, Richard found a place for them just far enough from the plantation, across the state line into Mississippi."

"This is quite a story, and I've got a part in this one, given I'm a direct descendant!" I added for good measure as we laughed.

"That's right!" she responded. "It's difficult to imagine what the things we sow will amount to over time – especially far beyond our lifetime. We tend not to give much significance to our actions. But repeated often enough, patterns of thought, behaviors, decisions – when combined with the strength of our convictions and resolve – eventually amount to something, or, as in the case of Richard's carvings, if he didn't stop at some point, he'd have nothing left at all!"

"That's an awful lot to sit with, Aunt Joni. You're describing me for sure. And whether I want to or not, you're causing me to think about where I'm going in my life!"

"Well," Aunt Joni replied, "Richard's own children weren't too far off at that point in his life. Somewhere deep inside of him were the elements within the elements of both you and me, which wouldn't surface for generations to come."

"I'm getting a glimpse of why it was important for me to visit, and we've really just gotten started," I interjected. "You're literally giving me an opportunity to learn about myself through all these relations. Weirdly, it makes me think of beautiful flowers!"

It was my aunt's chance to return a quizzical look. "Oh?" she replied, smiling.

"I loved going to the Portland Rose Gardens with Mom and Dad as a kid. I always knew I would be happy to see all the vibrant colors and be able to bury my nose in a bouquet of fragrance. It took me to a really great place inside – and made me sad to see them start to go. Yet each rose bush..." I paused, raising my finger. "...bears the buds of future flowers to come! Or something like that," I think I added, laughing.

"That's right," she responded. "Imagine, every day, their growth and development are influenced by many factors – the light, condition of their soil, moisture level, nutrients – all shape what they ultimately look like, what they grow to become! Imagine – you might hold the key to the lives of beautiful flowers two hundred years into the future, eh?"

"Yeah," I answered. "I haven't really thought much about life beyond my own, backward or forward in time."

"That's to be expected! People see what's in front of them – it's their frame of reference. Many never connect with the trail of history that brought them into the world – and similarly, they are not imagining the importance of the road they're paving into the future! Unfortunately, many, young and old alike, are also disconnected from the world around them, as if they are separate from everything and everyone else. Again, it's a matter of perspective."

"Whoa, Aunt Joni, that's a lot. What do you mean?" I asked, now knowing there had to be more to the tale.

"Do you feel the warmth of the air on your skin?"

"It's awesome here!"

"We human beings – our egos, really – fool ourselves into believing we're somehow separate from the rest of the world. Clearly, as many have pointed out to us over time, we couldn't exist for long without the blood inside us or the air around us – yet many still hold themselves as nothing more than separately identifying ego-beings contained within the boundaries of their own skin."

I was totally stunned. At that point in my life, I was now seeing my perspective described and mirrored back to me by my aunt.

"Yet the air around us is as much a part of us as anything inside ourselves. And as we travel through the world, it is our ever-present reminder that we are truly connected to everything – everything around us!"

There was a natural pause in our conversation. Eventually, the crickets began to sound off, adding a natural rhythm section to my delight.

"It was such a thrill to me when I began sharing *Torch Time Tales* with our family," she finally said. "I've rested easier knowing this tradition might make a difference. My life is more than my own! I have all my past relations and those who helped them to thank for the burdens they bore – without them, we wouldn't be here. And you, my dear one, hold the key to unlocking the door for the family to become what it will be." My aunt looked over to check my reaction.

"What?" I exclaimed, anxious at such a forecast.

"In fairness, we are still six generations ahead of ourselves in this tale now, aren't we?"

I couldn't help but laugh at that and nodded. Without a word, we rose from the bench, ready to call it a night.

* * *

I woke to light streaming through the room. I heard birds and caught glimpses of them darting around outside the open window. My head felt thick, and for a moment, I thought I was home in my room. Then I began to remember and sat up with a start. Was it yesterday or the day before that I'd arrived? No, I thought to myself, it was really three days ago that I'd left work to start the long drive to my aunt's place. Now, granted, I was just waking up, but with all the time travel we'd been doing, I have to tell you my own reality had already begun to get just a little fuzzy.

"You've slept half the day away!" she called from the next room. "You must still be exhausted from that long trip. And I bet you're ravenous from the golf!"

"I am!" I answered. "I'll be right out." I pulled on shorts and a t-shirt from my bag. A glimpse in the mirror confirmed pale skin framed by a mess of hair growing longer by the day. Emerging from the room, I found Aunt Joni waiting and the table set for breakfast.

"What time is it?" I asked, sitting down at the table.

"It's nearly noon!" she answered, smiling and joining me at the table.

After breakfast, we walked the neighborhood, visiting with neighbors and shopping at the local stores along the way. Eventually, we made it back to her house. I quickly discovered California life had its own cycles. The intense heat drove most to seek the relief of shade, a nap, or both.

My aunt had an outdoor set of chairs staged underneath the veranda, tucked behind the shade of the two enormous golden lotus banana trees just for that reason. Initially, Joni's realtor had introduced these two particular plants to her as banana palms, and my aunt had recognized the breathtaking flowers from her many trips to Thailand. It was some years before my ever-curious brother discovered the true dirt on these extraordinary creatures. Technically, they weren't palms at all but related to the banana tree family and also to the family of grasses by nature of their rhizome base. I'd never seen anything quite like them. They were truly amazing.

Refreshed by the cool of the shade, the two of us would soon be ready to have a meal and eventually make our way back out to one of the benches to pick up where my aunt had left off with the *Tales*.

"So, what happened to Richard and Cornelia?" I asked her as we sat down on the bench together that evening.

"After their wedding, Richard and Cornelia wasted no time beginning their own family together, my dear. Their first son was born on April 22, 1852, barely nine months later. That baby, Junius Brown Whitmore, was your great-great-grandfather. Brown was Cornelia's family name, you might recall. It was their way of honoring and remembering Cornelia's side of the family. His name was a bit of a mouthful, so they called him J.B. for short."

"Hey, that sounds familiar. Doesn't my father call you J.L.?"

"Yes, he does. And he's the only one in the family who ever used my initials to address me," she added in a manner that suggested he was the only one in the family who could have gotten away with it.

Before I could ask her anything more, she picked back up again. "Not long after that, President Fillmore was succeeded by our fourteenth president, Franklin Pierce, in 1853. Richard and Cornelia welcomed their second son, Richard Adolfus Whitmore, the following year of 1854, and then Thomas Whitmore was born two years later in the fall of 1856. Within five years of their marriage, Cornelia and Richard had three sons. They were off to a productive start, one might say, when tragedy struck hard."

"What happened?"

"In 1857, James Buchanan became the fifteenth president of the United States!" Aunt Joni responded without blinking an eye.

"What about Richard and Cornelia?" I persisted, not letting her off the hook.

"In the fall of the next year, 1858, Cornelia was pregnant again. By that point, she had three boys in tow – two, four, and six years old. The youngest, Thomas, contracted cholera, I suspect, that winter. It must have had an enormous impact on them to watch Thomas slip away. He died the following January, some twenty-eight months after his birth. Cornelia was five months pregnant with her fourth child when they buried Thomas. I found a memorial note to him in the family Bible, written by his father, Richard Augustus Whitmore."

"What did it say?" I asked, curious to hear what he might have written back then.

My aunt leafed through her notebook to the spot needed and read the inscription aloud.

Thomas Whitmore departed this life on the 26th day of January 1859, buried Hardeman County, Tenn. From Earth, his pure spirit hath taken its weary flight to God who gave it.

"God, is that sad!" I couldn't help but exclaim.

"Cornelia gave birth to their first daughter that spring of 1859. There was some discrepancy in the records, and for a while, I questioned whether she was named Inda or India."

"Inda?" I repeated. "I've never heard that name. What does it mean?"

"As it turns out, Inda is another English word for the country India," she replied. "It's clear that Richard and Cornelia's intent was to name her after the country. They may have called her Inda for short, which might have started the confusion in the historical family records. When I visited Grand Junction, Tennessee, and the Ames Institute, I was able to see with my own eyes another one of the handwritten notes in the family Bible from Richard and Cornelia regarding their beloved daughter India."

"So, why do you think they named her India?" I asked.

"I can't say for sure. I can only surmise. I do suspect that Cornelia was book-learned, as they would have said in those times, much like Richard. I just can't imagine him with a young woman who had nothing much to say to him. It's possible but not probable. No, I suspect she was well read for her young years. Neither of them had ever been to India – that much, I'm sure."

"But why would they have named her India?" I asked again. "That just seems odd to me."

"As a country, India is considered the birthplace of four of the world's major religions, Hinduism, Buddhism, Jainism, and Sikhism. I suspect the death of Thomas, followed by the birth of India three and a half months later, had a profound impact on them – it may have shaken the foundations of their spiritual world. And certainly, India holds a reputation for being the birthplace of many a wise sage through the ages."

"That's fascinating!" I couldn't help but respond.

"That takes me circling back to our conversation about the golden lotus flowers. Did I mention Buddha identified them as the king of celestial trees?"

"No, you didn't. But you lost me. What circle took you there?" I looked at my aunt quizzically as I attempted to follow this off-the-wall observation.

"We're talking about India. Sakyamuni Buddha was born in India."

"Sakya who?" I asked as I turned my attention toward following my aunt's train of thought.

"The Sage of the Sakya Clan is the literal English translation of his name from the Sanskrit or the local language of Pali, depending on your source material."

"I guess I'm not familiar with him."

"Does Siddhartha Gautama ring a bell, maybe from school?" she asked gingerly.

"Oh, yeah! That rings a bell. Maybe from English or history? I don't know. He was Buddha, right? The middle way and all that?"

"Siddhartha Gautama was his historical name. Sakyamuni Buddha is one of his many, many spiritual titles."

"Okay, so now I'll take you back to the circle within your circle, Aunt Joni. Why do you think Sakyamuni Buddha would have called the golden lotus the king of celestial trees?" I asked her, now ready to call her bluff and get an actual answer to what was becoming a list of seemingly unanswerable questions she continued to toss in my direction.

"There have been books written on that subject!" she responded with glee, and then, after a pause, she added simply, "They are self-replicating."

"Wow! That's way cool!" I responded, stunned by her quick response and this new information. "Can you say more?"

"Self-replication occurs in the coexisting natural and spiritual worlds, which is part of why Buddha made the analogy. And while we're here, can you name the four ways sentient beings are born into the world?"

"I'm not sure I can," I replied, shaking my head as I pondered the question.

"They'll all be familiar to you. Think this through. Chickens are born how?"

"They're egg-born, duh. Okay, so there's one."

"How about human beings?"

"Okay, that's easy; egg and sperm unite in the womb. They're womb-born."

"Very good. So, now you have two of them."

"You're going to have to help me, Aunt Joni, or we could be here a while," I responded with a smirk, just a little bit embarrassed to not know something so…basic!

"Okay, what type of birth do you get when you combine heat and moisture?" she asked.

"Oh…yeah! You're talking about creatures born in humidity, aren't you?"

"Yep! Okay, last but not least, here's a hint: what is the process that a butterfly uses?"

I scrunched up my face, and then out popped the answer. "Metamorphosis!" I cried, feeling like I'd won the lottery. We both laughed, me with relief.

"Are you satisfied with this sidetrack for the moment?" she asked me.

"Absolutely! Thank you for indulging me. That was more of an answer than I'd bargained for with my smart-aleck follow-up question."

"You are most welcome. It was a good question. And it seemed an important addition in the moment."

"So, where were we with Richard and Cornelia?

"I was about to tell you that Richard and Cornelia spent the first nine years of their married life together in Mississippi before deciding to uproot the family. Their daughter India was a year old when they left Mississippi and moved to DeWitt, Arkansas, in 1860," she continued after a sip.

"That's ironic," I noted. "The Whitmores moved to DeWitt?"

"Yes, indeed, the heart of the Mississippi River delta country in southeastern Arkansas, known for good farming and rice production to this day. Interestingly, that area has some serious history, which may have been its own draw for the young couple. The French established the first settlement west of the Mississippi there in 1686, known as the Arkansas Post."

"So, do you know why they moved?"

"Perhaps Richard wanted them to have a fresh start away from the painful memories of the place where they'd lost their son, or maybe he wanted to put a little more distance between himself and his father, Burwell – it was nearly 170 miles southwest of Grand Junction. Certainly, they had to consider that tempers were heating up politically over the future course of the country and what would soon be civil war. Then again, maybe Richard and Cornelia moved for warmer weather or better fishing!" she added in jest.

"Geez, Aunt Joni," I couldn't help teasing.

"Something caused them to go. We just don't know. Had it been forty years earlier, say 1822, Arkansas would have been considered the westernmost frontier of the United States. Between 1820 and 1830, most of the Native Americans still in the Arkansas Territory had been moved to Oklahoma, and purportedly many that remained attempted to pass as white. The Arkansas historical website acknowledges that the territory had been freed of all tribal property by 1828. The land was assumed by the government and moved back into private hands fairly rapidly, and it was then available for purchase. Fast forward thirty-plus years from that point, and it appears the couple wasted little time in beginning their new life together in Arkansas – and they did quite well for themselves. The weather was warmer, the winters easier, and the living fine for a growing family."

"What did they do?" I was curious to know.

"Richard began building on what he had learned in his life – from his father and his oldest sister, Sallie. He bought property, first one parcel and then another. Much of the land, he began to farm himself, something he knew how to do. At night, after the family settled down, he started studying the law – devouring everything he could get his hands on to better understand it."

"Farmer to lawyer seems like a big jump. It sounds like he was pretty motivated," I observed.

"Don't forget, he loved to learn, and his sister Sallie had made learning fun for him when he was a child. Only one year after they moved to Arkansas, in 1861 – one hundred years before I was born, to give you some perspective – Richard was awarded his license to practice law in chancery and circuit courts in Arkansas. The license was written longhand on tablet paper and signed by Judge J.C. Munay and Joseph Maxwell, court clerk.

"He became a lawyer?" I asked, still in disbelief.

"Yes, he did," she answered, "and purportedly, over the course of his remaining years, he became a highly regarded attorney. The story goes that in those days, before you could practice law in Arkansas, you had to swear on a stack of Bibles that you'd never fought in or been challenged to…a duel."

"Really? Why was that?" I asked, surprised. "And why do you think he became a lawyer?"

"Good questions. Let's take them one at a time. In building respect for the law and order of their civilization, such as it was, I suspect the aim was to attract peaceable folk to the task. Right or wrong, that law effectively eliminated the hotheads – those who had been prone to settling their disputes violently – from ever engaging in the legal practice! Engaging in dueling would have shown a level of contempt for the law and legal process."

"Wow! I had no idea. I'm imagining two Abe Lincoln types in tall hats, squared off in the middle of town, ready to fire at one another."

"As to why he became a lawyer, again, I can only surmise, and yet his life and the timing of his licensing give us ample clues." Aunt Joni paused for a moment to allow me time to digest her words.

"What do you mean?" I responded on cue. It wasn't obvious to me at all.

"Well," she said, "let's re-piece together what we know about Richard and place him in the historical context of the time in which he lived once again, shall we?"

"That would help me," I replied sheepishly. "I'm lost."

"No problem," she answered. "Remember how I mentioned that Richard's father, Burwell, had the forced labor of many enslaved people to develop his large estate?"

I nodded.

"It was common practice for plantation owners in those times to use pain and fear to coerce slaves into submitting to the owner's control and direction. Had there been great love and respect between the men, my guess is that Richard might have settled with his wife near his parents. But we know that's not what happened."

"I can't imagine what that would have been like for him," I said, trying to keep the images at bay.

"While he had his father's disposition toward violence to learn from on the one hand, he also had the contrasting behavior of his departed sister, Sallie. She'd been the mediator and peacemaker, if you will, of their childhood disputes. She stayed calm in the midst of their trials and tribulations as kids. And I suspect she had an evolved sense of right and wrong for her age, which she passed on to Richard."

"So, you're essentially telling me that his father and his sister had personalities at the opposite ends of the spectrum from one another?"

"Well said. Yes. It's also important to remember that Sallie, Richard, and especially their father, Burwell, would have all been influenced – for better or worse – by developments in the federal government growing up nearby them in Virginia even prior to their moves westward."

She paused for just a moment before going on. "Then I would point to the year of Richard's licensing as a lawyer in 1861, which I don't think is a coincidence. And one of your last analogies wasn't far off. That was the year one of America's most beloved sons, Abraham Lincoln, was sworn in as the sixteenth president of the United States!" Aunt Joni's eyebrows furrowed a bit. "Richard's boyhood state of Tennessee seceded from the Union that year as well," she remarked with a troubled tone in her voice.

I looked at her with one eyebrow raised. I'm embarrassed to admit I had no idea where she was headed.

"It was the first year of the Civil War," she begrudgingly noted. "It's been called a whole host of names over time, depending on one's location or perspective. The Northerners and their historians referred to it as the War of the Rebellion or simply the Great Rebellion, names I'd never heard before. In the Southern states, during the conflict, it was called the War for Southern Independence, and afterward, Southerners referred to it as the War Between the States, among others. Arkansas also joined the Confederacy that first year."

"Oh," I responded, shaking my head as I began to get a clue. She'd hinted at it just a few minutes ago.

"This war was fought over the Southern states' belief in their right to be independent – to do as they pleased, which, for them, included the institution and practice of slavery. The Southern landowners, by and large, wanted the practice maintained. It suited their selfish interests."

"That was a real crossroad for our country, wasn't it?"

"History tells us that even George Washington, one of our great patriots, didn't get around to freeing his own slaves until his last will and testament kicked in after his death. To his credit, he fought the uphill battle against slavery during his era, but sadly, he still personally benefited from the efforts of his slaves for the course of his entire privileged lifetime."

"Didn't he inherit his estate from his brother?" I asked, unsure of my facts.

"That rings a bell – it may have been his half-brother," she replied. "In our case, perhaps Richard was learned enough to see the futility of the war and wise enough to recognize that as one man, he couldn't prevent it. Historical records reveal that many of our clan fought and died in the Civil War – some for the Union and some for the Southern Confederacy! Our family battled one another on both sides of the war! Can you imagine the absurdity of that?" she asked me, throwing her hands up in the air.

"That's insane!" I replied. I immediately flashed to a large field with men from one side of the family lined up to fight against our own relations on the other side of the line. Wind rustling in the palm fronds beside us brought my attention back to our spot far to the west of those battles.

"Our family historical record suggests that more than one of our Confederate relations ended up serving time in prison after being captured in the war."

"I never knew that."

"It's so ironic," she said, sighing and shaking her head. "The Confederate prisoners of the Civil War were, in some cases, allowed to negotiate their own release through a transfer to a Union regiment. The Union then used these prisoners of war to fight Native Americans in the western regions of the country! I apologize for getting so worked up about all of this," she said, sharing a look of amazement over what had happened in our history.

"Wow! I'll say so. It gives me a totally different sense of the Civil War and our own clan to imagine family members on both sides of that line. Not to mention this idea that the 'good' guys in that fight wanted to free enslaved African Americans while simultaneously forcing Confederate prisoners of war to help the Union slaughter Native Americans. That's just fucking mind-blowing," I added in stunned amazement, and then I walked away.

This last historical bit had blown the lid off our conversation. I had to take a break so I could process this latest revelation. I had always assumed the Union forces were the good guys and the political and moral lines between the two sides were reasonably clear. Moral high ground, in this case, appeared to be more of a slippery slope than I might have ever imagined.

"It was absolutely okay to take a break to process all of this, absolutely okay," she affirmed later as we sat back down. "Don't hesitate to stop me at any point, okay?"

I nodded and smiled.

"So, back to Richard. His timely steps to become a lawyer positioned him in such a way that he could have some manner of influencing what was thought of as right from wrong during those dreadful times. Although, I must confess, I have not gotten to the bottom of my legal research where he's concerned to seriously form an opinion on his views. There may well be quite a bit more to find in that regard."

"Did you find anything?" I asked, now curious to hear what she'd actually found.

"Oh, yeah. We'll come back to his legal entanglements soon enough. Clearly, many of our family relations weren't so lucky in their chosen paths. Cousin Paula's research revealed a number of our relations had landed in Union prisons during the war, including Alton Prison, in Illinois, built to hold the ranks of soldiers who'd served the Confederacy."

"Can you give me an idea of how many family members were involved in the war on either side?"

"Nope, I can't. As it is, my mother's side has many more who were prominently involved in various wars, which you'll get to hear about in volume two."

"That's still just mind-boggling to me. They put these guys in prison but let them out if they agreed to fight for the other side?"

"You've got it right. The Union could not afford to have the Confederate troops rejoin their ranks. They had more battles on their hands than they were able to manage as it was. One relation from Dad's side that stood out for me was William Tasville Potter. Your grandfather William was named for his grandfather on his mother's side. He would have been my great-grandfather."

"Was he one of the captured Confederate soldiers who was imprisoned?" I inquired.

"Yes," she responded. "Cousin Paula received a copy of his entire war record from Cousin Helen's archive, I believe."

"No kidding!" I wondered what that might have looked like.

"He was held in three different military prisons," she added. "I'll spare you the gory details, but suffice it to say those prisons were hellholes."

I felt my entire face cringe in horror as I repeated what I'd just heard. "He was held in three different military prisons?"

"From what I gathered, he enlisted with one of his brothers-in-law in Lauratown, Arkansas. He was a private in Company A of Shaver's Regiment of the 38th Arkansas Infantry. About fifteen months later, in the summer of 1862, he must have gotten injured during battle. He was actually captured while in the hospital in Little

Rock, Arkansas, and sent to military prison in St Louis, Missouri, then to the military prison in Alton, Illinois, and then to Camp Douglas, also in Illinois. Not long after that, he was given the option to muster in with the 5th Volunteer Infantry of the US Army."

"That's unbelievable," I blurted out. "I'm amazed America survived the Civil War in one piece."

My aunt nodded in agreement. "We've got to backtrack now just a bit. I got ahead of myself, attempting to answer your good questions. During that spring of 1861, the first year of the war, Cornelia became pregnant for the fifth time. At this point, Junius would have been nine years old, Richard was seven, their third son, Thomas, had passed, and their daughter India was just two years old. Annie Nook Whitmore was born late that November."

"Nook?" I asked. "That's a strange middle name."

"Yes, it is," she agreed, "and I can imagine that she might have been so tiny that perhaps she could fit into almost any old nook or cranny around. Nicknames are common in our family!"

"Okay, so then what happened?" I prompted.

"The next year, 1862, the family was still living with the daily anxieties, unknowns, and constraints of the war, I'd imagine. Richard continued to work his legal practice and their land, and Cornelia oversaw the home front with a newborn baby and three growing young children underfoot. There was big news that September, when President Lincoln delivered the Emancipation Proclamation, which freed by some estimates more than three million slaves, but only those in the Confederate states."

"Wow! That's mind-blowing. I had no idea so many people had been enslaved."

"However, several months went by before his proclamation was actually printed and issued, and it revealed that sometime in between, President Lincoln had exempted Richard's home state of Tennessee."

"Why so? And why am I getting a sense that the plot is thickening?"

"The plot is thickening, and in more ways than I can describe at the moment. The future president Andrew Johnson served Tennessee in many capacities, including as governor in the 1850s. He was the only US senator from a Confederate state that did not resign when his state seceded from the Union. Lincoln had appointed him the military governor of Tennessee in March of 1862. Andrew Johnson was responsible for persuading Lincoln to exempt Tennessee from the proclamation on the grounds that, as Johnson had governed Tennessee, the state was not truly in 'rebellion' like the other Confederate states. He held the authority to be in the position to ask for and pull off that outrageous request!"

I really didn't know what to make of it all. I was getting an insider's view of history, and it sure looked different than anything I'd ever learned.

"The Emancipation Proclamation was a ray of hope. However, what followed it were difficult times for many, many people," she replied. "By October, about a month before Nook's first birthday, Richard and Cornelia's daughter India died. She was just three and half years old. I don't know how. I do know it must have been a horrible blow. At that age, she would have been a walking, talking little ball of loving energy – needed medicine for Cornelia's and Richard's hearts, if you will, following the death of their son Thomas and the travesties of the war around them."

I watched as her gaze moved momentarily back to me. "Wasn't there a memorial note to her in the family Bible you mentioned?"

"Yes, indeed. Well done. Well done!" my aunt responded. Again, she opened the notebook at just the right spot.

India Whitmore departed this life on the 12th day of October 1862. This sweet angel now dwells in Paradise. Buried at DeWitt, Arkansas Co, Ark.

"So, they buried Thomas in the family cemetery in Grand Junction, Tennessee, before they left Mississippi and then buried India after they moved to Arkansas," I repeated as a way to get clear on what I thought I'd heard.

"You've got it right. And the Civil War was still going on around them. By the following summer of 1863, the Union troops fully occupied Little Rock, the state capital. It was an extremely difficult and tense time. That fall, Cornelia became pregnant for the sixth time. If they were blessed with a girl, they planned to name her after her mother, Cornelia, and call her Nellie for short. By the following spring, in April of 1864, with the Civil War still blazing away, Cornelia did give birth to their third daughter."

"Also named Cornelia?" I was beginning to see how our family names appeared to repeat themselves.

"That's right. Did I remember to mention that President Lincoln ran for a second term that year with Andrew Johnson, who, you now know, hailed from Tennessee, as his vice-presidential running mate?"

Before I could even shake my head, she continued. "I'm getting ahead of myself, but as president, Johnson was a controversial man who bridged some horrendous times and then played a bit part in our family drama later on."

"You lost me again, I'm afraid," I added, trying to keep up with her.

"It's no problem! A lot happened quickly in our history. By 1865, the Civil War had ended, President Lincoln had been assassinated, and Richard and Cornelia continued to experience their own tragedies. Andrew Johnson was sworn in immediately as the country's seventeenth president on April 15."

"That's quite a bit," I agreed. "It sounds like a shitload of stress to have to live through, with the death of a child and that enormous political mess," I added for emphasis.

"Nook died just shy of her fourth birthday that fall. Out of their four youngest children, three had died before they were even four years old. And much like Richard's mother, Amanda Elder, Cornelia's spirits may have felt the depths of depression."

"Was there a memorial inscription for her as well?" I asked.

"Yes, there was. Let me look," Aunt Joni replied, opening her book.

Anna N. Whitmore departed this life on the 3rd day of October, AD 1865. She has joined her dear brother and sister in the realms of heaven. None dearer, none sweeter, more precious than she... Buried by the side of her dear sister India, DeWitt, Arkansas County, Arkansas.

"That's so beautiful and just so sad," I replied quietly.

My aunt took a sip of her beverage before continuing. "The two oldest boys, Junius Brown, or J.B., as they called him, your great-great-grandfather," she reminded me, "and his brother, Richard Adolfus, were thirteen and ten years old, respectively, the year their sister Nook died and the war was ended. They were old enough to get out of the house and leave their mother to her misery."

"What about their father?" I asked.

"Richard Augustus had the experience of realizing the pain his mother and father had lived through with the births and deaths of his own siblings. And despite himself, he, too, subsequently buried himself in his work, much like his father had, as a means to cope with the unbearable pain of their loss."

"Unbelievable," was all I could say.

"Truly," my Aunt Joni answered. "I can't imagine."

Praying Mantis on Golden Lotus. Photo by John Bajowski.

CHAPTER 4

Lighting the Torch

T he next day brought rain to the West Coast. It was a welcome relief from the hot climate, and we spent much of the day inside. Aunt Joni announced it was time to finish harvesting the garlic she'd planted last fall. I'd never grown garlic. Shit, I'd never even had a garden at that point in my life, so this was new and different – and in hindsight, pretty dang enjoyable.

She explained it had to be dug from underneath so as not to cause breakage between the clove and the green garlic shoots, which provided additional moisture for the clove while it was drying. The cloves, with their fronds still attached, were given a quick rinse after coming out of the ground and then bundled together and hung in a cool, shady spot inside to dry.

"Here we go," she said, placing a bowl overflowing with a mass of untrimmed garlic between us.

The fresh raw garlic now under my nose was enticingly strong. "Wow!" I exclaimed. "That smells great!"

Then, with a few scissor snips, she showed me how to cut the remains of the bottom roots off as close to the clove as possible and, with one or two more snips, remove the dried-out garlic fronds from the top of the clove. And voila! I was looking at a beautiful head of garlic plopped into the palm of my hand. With sixty seconds of instruction, I'd become a garlic trimmer.

Between the two of us, we made quick work of the sixty-three cloves she'd planted for the annual crop. By late afternoon, the sun had emerged, and the skyline turned a deep red when it eventually disappeared over the horizon.

"Are you ready for more, or would you rather take a break?" my aunt asked me after dinner.

"Are you kidding?" I replied. "These days are passing too fast as it is, and we've got too much ground to cover!"

"That's the spirit," she said with a smile, and the two of us headed outside.

It was cooler but still wonderfully comfortable. "So, what happened to Richard and Cornelia?" I asked.

"What I know is that some time passed after the war before Richard and Cornelia had any more children. I suspect they needed the time – time to heal, time to come back around to finding the love they had for one another again. Their sons, J.B. and Richard Adolfus, were growing up – and becoming strapping young men."

She paused just a moment. "By 1867, the worst of their bad fortune appeared behind them. It was an important year for the couple and another turning point. Cornelia was expecting again and, in February, gave birth to baby George Burwell Whitmore. Perhaps as a sign of respect for what Richard's own father had been through, George was given his middle name to acknowledge his grandfather." Again, she paused, but only for a moment.

I had to bite my tongue on that one. Whatever I might have said about Burwell Whitmore without thinking about it first would have been downright disrespectful at that point in my life.

"Not long after baby George was born, some pretty amazing news arrived. President Andrew Johnson appointed Richard to serve a lifetime post as a United States circuit court judge for the State of Arkansas. Under almost any other set of circumstances, the honor would have been enormous. Richard had reached the pinnacle of his legal career – and according to the historical article by Arkansas writer Virginia Fuller, he was at that time considered one of the best lawyers in the state. While he was initially flattered and taken with the idea, he ultimately turned down the post."

"Why did he turn it down?" I asked.

"The newspaper article seemed to indicate it was because of the times. The era following the Civil War was called the Reconstruction Period. The war was over, but there was still great unrest and injustices occurring in the South that would continue unabated for another hundred-plus years. While all of that is true, I'm not sure those were the primary reasons he declined."

"What do you think?"

"I think he realized that it would take him away from his wife and their newborn son for long periods at a point in which her emotional health was still fragile. After the loss of three children, I suspect she was a vulnerable soul. I'd say his decision to turn down an appointment from the president to care for the most important people in his life may have been extraordinarily selfless."

"That would have been a tough decision for anybody, I would think."

"It is also possible Richard wanted to distance himself from Andrew Johnson's administration, which overlooked a lot of what had happened in their eagerness to patch things up with the Southern states. People were let off the hook for horrible transgressions. Historians view him as one of the worst presidents in history. He was impeached by the House of Representatives for racist speech, and he held slaves himself. He ultimately opposed the Fourteenth Amendment to the Constitution, which insured that formerly enslaved people were given the rights of citizenship and guaranteed all citizens equal protection under the law. America has relied on the Equal Protection Clause to advance."

"Well, you have to admit, Johnson had some serious competition for that inauspicious ranking in the twenty-first century," I replied, shaking my head. I got no argument from my aunt on that one.

The voters in the United States had shown the last one, with great difficulty, to the door. We were all recovering from post-traumatic election shock laced with ongoing COVID-19 pandemic duress and restrictions. Our nation was perhaps more greatly divided than ever. I couldn't help but wonder if the scars of the Civil War hadn't planted at least some of the seeds for the crop of results we were harvesting now. The entire world had seemingly been changed overnight.

"Had Richard accepted President Johnson's appointment to the bench, he would have been in a key position to do the president's bidding in Arkansas, which included letting greedy Southern landowners, politicians, and their ilk off the hook for their egregious actions. Our country will never know what might have transpired differently after the close of the war had President Lincoln been able to continue his nation-changing work." She shook her head. "Yet even he, evidently, felt forced to make horrible compromises, as he did with Johnson and the South generally, to keep the founders' vision of the country in sight. I'd offer that while Lincoln was a great man who gave his life for this country, realistically, he wasn't a miracle worker."

"Wait a minute, Aunt Joni. Help me understand. What more could he have achieved if he'd lived?"

"As commander in chief, he showed himself to have a stronger backbone than President Johnson ever had, and perhaps he could have overseen and made more progress toward the actual implementation of liberty and justice for all!"

"Okay, okay. One more minute. Back to Richard. It was quite an honor for him to be asked, wasn't it?"

Aunt Joni didn't respond immediately. Then she grimaced.

"I think that is questionable. Richard may have surmised that his own talents may not have been the driving force behind the offer and that it was likely his father, Burwell, had been involved. And he may not have agreed with the reasons his father wanted him on the Arkansas bench."

"Wow, that's an interesting train of thought," I responded.

"Tennessee is a small state. Burwell and Andrew Johnson both lived there for decades. It stands to reason Burwell was probably well acquainted with Andrew Johnson in his elected capacities for Tennessee even prior to his becoming vice president. I think it's safe to assume Burwell and other slave owners were behind Johnson's push to get Lincoln to exempt Tennessee as a Confederate state from the Emancipation Proclamation when it was finally issued."

"That really makes a lot of sense," I responded. Oregon and Washington, states I was familiar with, were far larger in area than Tennessee, but they were similar to it in many ways, full of small towns – outside of the bigger cities, most everyone knew or knew of one another.

"Andrew Johnson was known in many circles as a hothead. One of his presidential predecessors from Tennessee, President Polk, publicly declared Johnson an irascible individual. Yep, I suspect Andrew and Burwell may have been well acquainted. Think about it. Johnson must have trusted Burwell enough to believe he could get his son to do Johnson's bidding or have known and trusted Richard enough himself to have extended him a lifetime bench appointment."

"I see what you mean. That's amazing!"

"I can't help but conclude that Richard Augustus Whitmore had no prior knowledge of or involvement in the judicial offer. Had he wanted the job or previously agreed to take it, he would have done so! I think it became clear to him that his father, Burwell, and President Andrew Johnson were looking for judges who would do the massive amount of dirty work necessary to let those slave-owning compatriots of theirs from Arkansas off the hook."

"That does seem to follow. Maybe it wasn't such a tough decision for him after all?"

"I'll interrupt to point out how interrelated all of this really is, and I'll add that our tales with respect to President Johnson's administration are not yet finished. But that will have to wait until the second or third volume." She chuckled. "Probably the third…"

"You're kidding, right?"

"No, I'm not. Otherwise, we'll get way too sidetracked by the shift in the space-time continuum, and I'll be at risk of losing this train of thought!" my aunt declared, again laughing at herself.

"Okay, okay, so do you remember where you left off?"

"I can tell you that in 1869, Ulysses S. Grant was sworn in as America's eighteenth president. And the next couple of years must have been happy and productive ones for the couple. Cornelia gave birth to another son, Joseph Chrisman Whitmore, who would one day outlive all his older siblings. Richard and Cornelia had toddlers underfoot once again. It must have brought back bittersweet memories for the couple – and of their children, both living and those who'd passed beyond."

The night air moved gently, and I watched my aunt's gaze shift to the stars.

"And perhaps the offer of a presidential appointment to the bench did give Richard the lift he needed to take his legal work to another level in a manner compatible with their family life together," she added after the pause. "In 1871, Richard was awarded a license to practice in front of the Supreme Court of Arkansas! That license was signed by W.M. Harrison, an associate justice of the Supreme Court, one of his clerks – N.W. Cox – and Alexander C. Wiley, a clerk of the circuit court.

"That's pretty huge, isn't it?" I asked, impressed by this additional news.

Aunt Joni nodded. "For her part, Cornelia was not finished yet, either. That winter, she became pregnant for the last time. In the span of five years, from 1867 to 1872, Cornelia and Richard had three more sons, bringing the total number of children she bore to nine. Six of their children would live into adulthood, the two oldest and the four youngest. Her middle three children all predeceased her. Edmund Justin Whitmore was born the year Cornelia turned forty and Richard forty-nine."

"I can't imagine having nine kids," I replied, shaking my head, privately scared out of my wits that I might meet such a fate in my own life.

"Quite common in those days, my dear," answered my aunt, "quite common. Birth control was widely available by that point, believe it or not, but it was frowned upon. By 1873, the year after

Cornelia bore her last child, Congress had passed the Comstock Laws, attempting to outlaw all forms of contraception."

"What do you mean, they attempted to outlaw them?" I asked suspiciously.

"The law could not be enforced. Humorously, it's been pointed out by more than a few, that was a battle our famous general-turned-president Ulysses S. Grant was sure to lose! There was more than ample demand." She laughed. "Instead of selling 'birth control,' the companies that made the various devices marketed them as feminine hygiene products – which hadn't been outlawed!"

My aunt continued laughing as she saw the look of shock hit my face. I was almost too stunned to speak.

"Are you serious? Are you telling me that truth in advertising has its roots in fake fucking marketing?"

"No pun intended, right? We were talking about birth control, after all," she retorted, smiling.

Aunt Joni had a quick wit about her – I have to give her that.

"Across these tales, ignorance and errors in judgment resulting from inaccurate information, translation, and interpretation, otherwise referred to in modern terms under the catch-all category of 'fake news,' come glaring through the history of the world. So much is still believed to be true to this day – all for lack of an accurate and credible accounting of what actually happened. There are a lot of sacred cows in this world of fake news, I will say, some more so than others!"

"And countless examples, I'm sure! You're on a roll, Aunt Joni. Keep going!"

"But more to your original point, it took a lot more labor to maintain a family in those days. There weren't all the conveniences we have today. And children didn't always make it, as we've seen in our own family. While it meant one more mouth to feed, it also meant two more hands to help with everything required for a family to survive, much less thrive. So, people kept it up!" she concluded, still trying to keep a straight face.

At that, I had to laugh out loud again. "I can't imagine living back then," I said, shaking my head.

"I'm beginning to imagine my bed is calling me," she responded, smiling as she began to yawn.

CHAPTER 5

Foreshadowing the Future

The next day dawned clear and hot. We were sitting on the back porch, enjoying our morning coffee, when I noticed a flash of blue and white come flying by around the side corner of the house. Within moments, I could hear water splashing, like something was taking a bath. I looked at my aunt with a quizzical expression.

"It's one of the blue jays in for a morning bath while the water's still cool," she said with a smile. "If you walk to the far side of the table underneath the pergola there, they'll tolerate your observation."

I followed her cue and walked out to the wrought-iron tables shaded overhead by the wisteria, sitting down in a spot that gave me line of sight to the private birdbath she'd arranged on the side of the house. I watched as the jay hopped in and out, in and out, and in and out so many times I lost count until it finally jumped in and completely submerged itself.

Periodic squawks of delight continued, with water flying everywhere. When the jay was finally finished, it perched on the side of the bath briefly and gave a quick shake before flying straight up into the sycamore, where it shook some more and then used its foot to scratch behind its head. At that moment, I would have sworn I was seeing a soaking-wet miniature dog in that tree. God, did I laugh! I looked over to see my aunt smiling and nodding.

"So, you've now been officially introduced to our jay family," Joni offered. "Perhaps they'll let you watch some of their other escapades while you're here."

"Oh?"

"In this case, you'll have to see to believe."

"Okay," I answered, silently wondering what the hell would come next!

"This place sat vacant for a couple of months before we bought it, and the jays enjoyed the place to themselves. When we showed up, they initially reflected their extreme displeasure in having us in the yard at all."

"Oh? How so?"

"It was hard to miss! They would screech unhappily and fly at us as if they were going to dive-bomb our heads."

I couldn't help chuckling a bit at the image of buying a new house and discovering it had dive-bombing residents. "So, how did you get them to stop?"

"It was obvious to me we had not been properly introduced and the relationship had gotten off to a horrible start. A peace offering was in order. So, I improvised by building them a proper bath, which I've maintained for all of our peace of mind. They really appreciate it, and so do I!"

"Cross-species diplomacy in action, eh?" I teased her.

"That's right! What do you say we take it easy this afternoon?" Aunt Joni asked me, changing the subject. "It might not be a bad idea to stay out of the sun today."

"That sounds fine," I answered. "Although I'm getting a pretty good tan, aren't I?"

"As a matter of fact, you are – and now that you have some color, I suspect it won't be as dangerous to be out for a bit midday."

We watched the golfers make the turn toward the championship-level, eighteenth-hole blue tees. The players would have to clear the entire line of oaks and the pond to make the shot to the fairway beyond. I heard the now-familiar thud of a golf ball colliding with one of the giant oaks, followed by the golfer cussing at himself in annoyance.

With that, we headed back inside for what turned out to be a good-sized brunch. Afterward, I made the mistake of stretching out on one of the full-length couches in the living room to relax.

* * *

I opened my eyes to realize I'd fallen asleep. Aunt Joni greeted me with a wave and headed toward the kitchen. "How are you?" I asked her gently.

"All considering, really pretty good," she responded. "How are you?"

"I must have needed that nap! I was dreaming I was golfing with my brother." I sat upright and began to stretch. "That makes me remember. He mentioned you'd had some serious health issues in the last few years, but he didn't really elaborate."

That observation got no response from her.

"He said it would be better if I asked you about it myself."

"I've already nominated your brother for sainthood!" she said with a big smile. "He's had to put up with your father, you, your other brother, and me!"

I laughed at her response. There was some truth to it. Our family had been through an awful lot. My brother and I were finally getting to the point of being solid with one another after a lifetime of struggling to get there. We'd spent years arguing. It really didn't matter about the subject. I'd been trying to find the right time to ask her about her health, hoping she might bring it up, but the opportunity never seemed to present itself.

"I had a traumatic, stress-induced heart attack in the fall of 2017," she said. "My heart was largely able to recover within several months. But instead of getting better, with each passing month, I became more seriously ill, and my blood pressure levels began rising significantly beyond their usually low range. In the fall of 2018, my neurologist gave me two months to two years to live if they couldn't figure out how to control my blood pressure."

"Holy cow!" I interjected. It was all that I could find to say to her in the moment. What do you say to someone who's been given a death sentence? I emitted a soft whistle and shook my head. I finally managed to get out an "I'm so sorry." And I was. At the point she shared her news, I felt the emotional blow land with a sense of the suddenness of the foreboding loss of her life that would inevitably come. These were far more precious moments than I could begin to comprehend. I was so thankful I'd finally gotten up the guts to ask her that question. In the scope of what she was attempting to accomplish with me, it was overdue.

"No reason to be sorry," she replied. "There's a bunch to be learned about this topic, that's for sure. Much to my dismay, when I began to try to educate myself about what had happened, I discovered very little had been learned since takotsubo myocardial infarctions were identified and named by Japanese doctors more than two decades ago. To make matters worse, my own health care provider network had been treating me with meds used for those with blockage-style heart attacks and refused to take me off of them even as my condition continued to markedly deteriorate with each passing month."

"That's horrible! How is it that you're still here?"

"Long story short, I wouldn't be if a cardiologist and a pharmacist at UCSF Medical hadn't helped me save my own life," she responded calmly. "In March of 2019, the *European Heart Journal* published a breakthrough study about traumatic, stress-induced heart attacks, detailing how our fight-or-flight system gets damaged in the process. That was when takotsubo syndrome was named."

"Huh? What's that?" I asked, teetering on overload with all the unfamiliar terminology.

"It's the condition that those of us who've experienced this type of heart attack are left with," she explained. "Without medication, my system can't calm down from any kind of exogenous shock, stressor, or provocation. My blood pressure spikes, and I might have another myocardial infarction or potentially even congestive heart failure. The abnormal heart rhythms are caused by the adrenergic system's impact on blood pressure, which can wreak havoc on my heart."

"Adrenergic system? Wait. What's that again?"

"That's our fight-or-flight system. It includes communication with the limbic system in the brain, our adrenal glands and kidneys, our blood pressure, and ultimately, our hearts. Damage to the limbic system's neurotransmitters prevents the rest of the adrenergic system from getting the signals the organs need to bring the blood pressure back down."

"That's an awful lot to try to understand, but I think I'm getting the drift. I appreciate your trying to explain it to me."

"Enough on that. How about if we switch gears and come back to this topic another time?"

"Okay," I responded, adding it to my growing list with her. "Thanks for sharing, Joni. It just underscores for me the importance of being here now."

"You are most welcome. It's a pleasure to have you here. And I so appreciate your help!"

* * *

"So, is there more to the tale of Richard and Cornelia?" I asked as we sat down that evening on the bench. The warm breeze carried the aroma of foods being prepared on the barbeque grills of the neighbors nearby.

"Where did we leave off?" Aunt Joni scratched her head and looked at me quizzically.

"We were talking about how they tried to outlaw contraception and the rise of fake fucking news. How could you forget?" I threw back at her. I suspected she knew full well where we'd left off but was checking to see if I had been paying attention. That trait seems to run in the family.

"Ah, yes," she replied. "it was 1873 or thereabouts. President Grant was still in office," she added after thinking about it for a moment. "Well, let's see. By that point, two of their children had become adults: Junius Brown was twenty-one, and Richard Adolfus would have been nineteen. Of their younger set, Nellie was the oldest to help look after the passel of boys. George was five, Joseph was about three, and Edmund would have been about a year old."

"It sounds like a houseful," I suggested.

"You can imagine it must have been tight quarters for all of them. I discovered much later that Junius moved out of the house that year."

"How did you figure that out?" I asked with my face scrunched in disbelief.

"It's a story in itself! You will understand more as we get farther into what happened. Let me say for now that this particular detail was from his father's firsthand testimony."

"Firsthand testimony?" I queried her in disbelief. "How did you happen upon firsthand testimony?"

"Then I put two and two together and realized Junius's brother Richard probably moved out with him. They would have found work and a place to live together. Within two years of that point, according to the handwritten entry in the family Bible made by their father, Richard Augustus Whitmore, his second son, Richard Adolfus Whitmore, married Katie Belknap on August 28, 1875. He would have been twenty-one by then and more than old enough to establish his own household."

"Firsthand testimony?" I asked, repeating the question for the third time.

"Okay, okay, yes, the family was involved in more than one lawsuit. That is how I also know that Junius lived apart from his parents for another couple of years before moving back in with the family at about twenty-five years old."

"More than one lawsuit?" I interjected incredulously.

"You are getting the picture!" my aunt replied with a smile. "As for Cornelia, she would have had her hands full – she was on her own much of the time with the youngsters while Richard practiced in front of the Arkansas Supreme Court."

"That's right!" I nodded, remembering what she had shared.

"The Arkansas Supreme Court was in Little Rock. By car nowadays, that trip from De Witt to Little Rock would take a couple of hours. Hard to say how long the trip took him in those days, but I suspect getting there and back on a regular basis consumed much of his time and he was gone from home a lot."

"Hmm," I wondered aloud. She was leaving me with more questions than answers.

"He would have been building his legal practice. I eventually began doing follow-up research to glean what I might about his character from his legal record. My initial call to one of the many Arkansas historical archives only turned up one case he worked on in 1879. With a little persistence, however, that spigot of new information eventually became more like a floodgate."

"That explains a lot. What was the 1879 case about?"

"The Mock versus Pleasants case was a fairly involved property dispute. The woman, Mrs. Pleasants, paid Richard one hundred dollars to represent her. At some point during those proceedings, he was replaced by another attorney."

"That's curious."

"My initial read left me with the impression that the woman involved had not acted with integrity with respect to her situation. She was the administrator of her husband's estate. They owed Mr. Mock money. If I recall correctly, it did not end well for her with the other attorney. She may have fired Richard because she didn't like his advice. It's also possible he resigned if he felt he could not honestly represent her."

"Hmm."

"That takes us to 1880, the year Richard and Cornelia decided to move the family to Little Rock so that they could spend more time together and he could continue his legal work without the long commute. Junius, who was twenty-eight, was back in their household to move with them. Their twenty-six-year-old son, Richard Adolfus, had already married and gone. Their daughter, Nellie, was sixteen, and their younger boys, who were twelve, ten, and eight by then, would have all benefited from better schools in Little Rock."

"And which administration were we in?" I asked, curious to see if she'd remember.

"That was toward the end of Rutherford Hayes's term, our nineteenth president," she added, thanking me for the reminder. "Before I forget to mention, Hayes oversaw the end of the Reconstruction period and was, by all accounts, considered an active reformer."

"I don't remember him," I replied sheepishly.

"I'd suggest he's one worth remembering!" She chuckled. "President Hayes believed in the equal advancement of all races."

"I had no idea!" I responded, again wondering how this guy had managed to slip by me.

"He supported education and work experience as a means to that end. He was clear about civil rights and human development. I give him a lot of credit. He understood the need for the right kind of restoration programs for the times."

"Wow! I'll say so. Thanks for bringing him to my attention, Aunt Joni."

"Significantly, some suggest he may have been the first president to warn America her government was in jeopardy if the concentration of wealth and power in the hands of a few continued at the expense of everyone else – who would be unable to afford an education, buy a home, or have hope of ever retiring."

"That guy appears to have been way ahead of his time. But now I'm sure I must have been sleeping through my history classes," I offered as a means to explain the gaps in my education and memory.

"Don't be embarrassed – very few people could talk knowledgeably about Rutherford Hayes. It would be roughly forty years before the ultra-wealthy came to terms with President Hayes's earlier projections, agreeing to a national income tax to be administered by the IRS as a means to begin to address the already-problematic massive gaps in societal wealth. It was another hundred years later, well into the twenty-first century, before America began acknowledging that our public school curriculums and textbooks had been largely literally whitewashed of much of the stain we've left on our collective historical development."

"That's just pathetically amazing!" I blurted out. "It explains so much. Okay, so you left off with President Hayes foreshadowing the future."

"Oh, how prophetic he was," she continued. "It appears America even then may have already passed the point of no return. Fast forward to 2012, and estimates emerged that half of all Americans would be unable to retire by age sixty-five, having been unable to save anything over their lifetimes. Paycheck chains, they began to call them! A different form of indentured servitude. By 2020, some sixty percent of Americans couldn't cover a one-thousand-dollar emergency. As you know, that was the year the horrific pandemic hit the world. Governments had to bail out numerous industries and households to the tune of trillions of dollars to help those that were otherwise unprepared."

"I'm even more embarrassed to say I couldn't tell you who followed President Rutherford Hayes," I responded humbly, repeating his full name out loud to help myself retain it.

"That may be because our twentieth president served all of two hundred days," she replied, trying to let me off the hook. "James Garfield was sworn in March of 1881, shot by an assassin in July, and dead by that September."

"Oh! Maybe that explains it!" I added, shaking my head. "Okay, so you were starting to tell me more about Richard and Cornelia when we got sidetracked."

"Well, I mentioned that Richard had started carving as a young boy, didn't I?"

"Yep," I replied. She'd thrown me a softball.

"Little Rock gave Richard access to new materials, and he began to experiment a bit. The carving gave him some balance in his life, I suspect – provided him some reflective quiet time that required a very different set of skills than practicing law. And as with much of what he did, he put his heart into it – when he could spare the moments. He got good at it as the decades went by. He carved statuettes out of sandstone and marble and even made musical instruments – I suspect by popular demand!"

"He did?" I asked incredulously. Our family had more talent than I might have imagined.

"Yep," my aunt responded. "He made handcrafted guitars and violins!"

"That's so cool!"

"I'd say that's hot!" She laughed. "You get the picture that your great-great-great-grandfather was a multi-talented man. But I'm getting ahead of myself, aren't I?"

"Yep. About four generations," I added, being a smart-ass.

"You can also imagine that there was a lot going on in Little Rock. As the state capital, it was a happening place. Richard began receiving unflattering comments from his clients about his son Junius Brown. He didn't give it much thought, chalking it up to the wild oats of youth. His boys had spent an awful lot of years in the country. There was a different life available to them in the big city."

I gave her a quizzical look.

"But it was the well-placed hints from his legal colleagues that really got his attention. It was not long after that he caught a glimpse himself as he made his way home from the office one evening."

"What do you mean? What did Richard see? What was Junius doing?"

"He was drunk, disorderly, and disrespectful to the fine ladies of Little Rock! Junius was old enough to know better. Given Richard's legal stature in the community and state at large, I suspect it caused him some amount of embarrassment!"

I looked at my father's sister, and she looked back at me, expressing with her eyes and brows what words could not.

"And before I forget to mention, Grover Cleveland began his first term as president in 1885. He served as our twenty-second and later as our twenty-fourth president."

"Grover Cleveland was 1885," I muttered to myself. "But what about Junius?"

"Let's just say Junius had not yet proven himself to his father. He caught work as he could around the area and then headed out in the evenings to party his pants off in Little Rock! Richard had been gone a lot during the years Junius was growing up. He probably held himself responsible for the state of his son's delinquent character. I guess Richard finally decided it was time to try to do something about it."

"What do you mean?" I asked innocently as I tried hard not to think about my own delinquencies in life. My aunt knew more than she was letting on.

"Richard had just finished a lengthy case, and his client owed him money. After due time waiting for payment, Richard agreed to terms. It was at about that point that he made his son Junius an offer."

"What was it?" I prompted her, feeling like I'd gotten off the hook somehow once again.

"The client had mentioned a neighbor of his just south of Little Rock who had a reasonably priced wagon and a team of mules for sale. It occurred to Richard that the mule team might provide Junius an opportunity for gainful employment. As his client was headed home for the weekend, Richard made arrangements to be introduced to the neighbor."

"That was thoughtful of him."

"That Saturday morning, Richard had to roust a hungover Junius out of bed. He'd hired a driver who would take the two of them to Tatumville, in Saline County. The driver arrived at the appointed time to pick up the two men. Junius didn't have much to say, still waking up and all, so Richard chatted up the driver as they made their way out of town into the country."

There had been more than a few occasions in my life when I'd woken up with a hangover. I found myself commiserating with Junius, who'd had to sit through a bumpy cart ride while feeling like shit. I watched and waited as Joni paused to eat a cookie.

"Richard's client received them at his home and, as agreed, walked them down the street a short way to the store, where he introduced them to the proprietor, Mr. J.W. Tatum. Then he bid them all a good day so they could get about their business. The wagon hitched with the mules was parked out front with a for-sale sign attached. After they had a chance to look over the team and the wagon, Mr. Tatum invited them into the store for a cup of coffee. And with that, the three men sat down and got to know one another a bit, I'd guess."

"So, they bought the mules and wagon?" I asked her.

"Yes, Richard purchased the team from Tatum that afternoon. As it turns out, that was the least of it. Tatum gave them quite a bit more than that to consider."

"What do you mean?"

"In the course of the conversation, it came out that it wasn't just the mule team and wagon for sale. Tatum was looking to offload his entire spread of land and the store."

"How could you know that?"

"I'd really get ahead of myself to tell you that," she replied. "At that point, Richard thanked the man for his offer and responded that, as it was, his legal practice, wife, and family demanded his full attention but he would take Mr. Tatum's offer into consideration. Not long after that, back in Little Rock, Richard sat Junius Brown down with the family and had quite a conversation. In short, he eventually made Junius an offer he couldn't refuse."

"What was it?" I asked.

"He was proposing to accept Mr. Tatum's offer, but only under certain conditions would he agree to give up his law practice and retire to the country. He proposed to Junius, as the oldest son, that Mom and Dad would agree to Mr. Tatum's terms if and only if Junius and his brothers would take it on as their own enterprise and work the place to make it pay for itself."

"Okay, Aunt Joni, once again, it begs the question, how could you possibly know that?" I asked her skeptically.

"I'm privy to a direct quote from Richard himself," she said and then read from her notes:

When the boys were persuading me to trade for the land, I told them that if I moved out there, they would have to take charge of the place, and work it, and furnish me shelter and board and clothing, as I could not make anything at my profession.

"Wow! It's amazing to hear his actual words! Where did that quote come from?" I asked.

"Good question. Hold on to it. It'll be clear soon enough."

"Okay, okay, go on."

"I was just going to share that the property was in bad shape and needed work. Richard's suggestion was to work toward a post office to go along with the store, with residences for the family above. He was about sixty years old at that point and must have hoped to retire. But that would take time and resources. If they were to grow cotton as well, it might be enough for the boys to cover the annual payments."

"How much did the guy want for the place?"

"All told, with a sizable amount of acreage and the existing store, Mr. Tatum was asking a bit more than a thousand dollars."

"That had to be boatloads for back then!" I remarked in surprise.

"Richard was blunt with his family. As it stood, there wasn't money for a down payment. It appears that while Richard's practice had afforded them resources to sustain residing in Little Rock, the bulk of the money he earned had been absorbed by the higher cost of living there. His legal work and family took up most of every day he had – and largely kept him in the city. So, he offered his sons a partnership if they were so inclined to take ownership of the place – and he set some expectations and limits from the get-go, I might add, about their efforts as well as his own involvement."

"So, this guy Tatum sells them a big spread with nothing down?" I asked, amazed that something like that could even be done.

"Richard and Cornelia provided him a handwritten note of obligation – a 'written obligatory,' I think they called it – followed by a mortgage with a lien on the property to secure the purchase monies. They agreed to make the first payment of $258.75 one year later, with three more annual payments to follow."

"That was enough?"

"Evidently, Mr. Tatum may have been persuaded by Richard's being an attorney. As a professional versed and licensed in the law, Mr. Tatum may have assumed he'd be as good as his word. He may have also needed somebody to help him look after the place. If I remember correctly, he was out of the area when his attorneys filed the first lawsuit. I'll tell you more about that later. He might have wanted the capital from the deal to use someplace else. To come back to your question, for him to have someone on the property committed to tending and working it and simultaneously paying him for it would have been a way for him to meet both goals."

"So, what did his sons say to Richard's offer?"

"How could they say no? It was a business venture made to order and handed to them on a silver platter! They didn't even have to think about it. All they had to do was show up and do the work. Richard was counting on it. If he could keep them at it, perhaps Junius Brown wouldn't have so much time to get in trouble!"

"Did it work?"

"Sort of," my aunt declared, clearly losing her steam.

It was later than I realized. I looked up into the southern night sky in time to catch sight of a luminous falling star before it vanished. I turned my head to see and confirm that my aunt had a big smile on her face as well.

CHAPTER 6

Double Trouble Served on Silver

I remember waking at dawn the next day. It was clear but not as hot. It was market day, and the two of us eventually ambled our way down to the local store to pick up produce and seafood for dinner. My aunt made a coconut milk and curry fish dish with rice that I had come to love as much as she did. Then we treated ourselves to ice cream, another family favorite.

After the dishes were done, we headed out the back door to the patio. The sun had just set, leaving the sky aglow with fiery streaks of light. Our time together on the bench was the highlight of the day. To a passerby, it would have been hard to tell who was enjoying themselves more – me or Aunt Joni.

"Well?" I asked after I had gotten the torch lit and we had settled ourselves on the bench. "Did Richard's plan work?"

"What was my answer last night when you asked me?" she asked in response.

"You said, 'Sort of,' but you didn't say anything more."

"No, the answer was too much to get into, given the late hour. In fairness, I felt this part deserved a fresh start. And I think the heat from yesterday must have worn me out. As I started to tell you, Richard's plan did not work out as imagined. However, Tatum and Richard must have made some form of verbal agreement that same year. The article I mentioned by Virginia Fuller about Richard relayed he retired to Tatumville in 1885. And it might have taken a while for Junius and his brother George to rehab the property. They started with getting the existing building into shape to accommodate the post office with a separate entrance."

"You weren't kidding me! Richard literally put them to work!"

"Then the pair of younger men had to double their pace – and split their efforts. They were simultaneously running the store and working on getting the post office finished while building living quarters upstairs before winter."

"It sounds like they would have been working round the clock to get all of that done."

"They would have planted their first cotton crop sometime in January of 1886, with the expectation of a July harvest, from what I understand of the process."

"No kidding! They planted cotton!" I replied, for some reason surprised.

"That spring, by April of 1886, Richard and Cornelia had worked out a formalized deal with Tatum to purchase the landholdings and the building, with a lien against the property to secure the purchase monies, as I mentioned. So, within a short time, they were officially in business. J.B. and George had their hands full overseeing their operations. Occasionally, their brother R.A. would come out to visit and help, but he had his own family by that point."

"So, they made a go of it, huh?" I asked.

"They tried," she responded. "It doesn't appear their first cotton crop amounted to much. I think Richard conveyed they managed two bales off their first year's attempt."

"That doesn't sound like much."

"The crop of 1887, they did much better. They must have doubled their efforts or gotten more rain or something, as they managed five bales that year."

"They more than doubled their output?"

"All four of Richard's boys would have been a year older and stronger. If I'm remembering correctly, Richard later made a reference to hired hands they'd employed to finish off that crop. That would have made a big difference, and they were all motivated! But with everything they had going on and as hard as they were working, Junius and George were soon chafing for time off. They were looking to their mom and dad to provide them some relief with the operations – and generously wanted to give their younger brothers, Joe and Edmund, a chance to learn the ropes of the operation as well."

"That doesn't sound so bad, but I still don't get your original answer – why did Richard's plan just sort of work?" I asked, still trying to get her to explain herself.

"It's complicated," she responded. "I'm trying to set the stage. The area was far enough out of town to be a little bit on the rough-and-tumble side. And while the local residents appreciated the convenience of a store and post office that saved them the trip to Little Rock, they were dealing with more traffic than they had before the Whitmore establishments opened. With the traffic came the usual array of problems, and before he knew it, Richard was pressed into service by the town fathers to become the justice of the peace! Cornelia was against it, but the townsfolk didn't give him an option. His businesses were the cause of the traffic and problems that ensued, and as a retired attorney well versed in the law, he was the obvious candidate for the job. Much like the proposition he'd put to his sons, the community wouldn't take no for an answer!"

"Oh, how interesting!" I uttered as I began to imagine Richard in cowboy boots, with a ten-gallon hat and a silver star on his vest.

"Well, no surprise, Richard thrived on it all. He loved the challenges and was used to the workload. He helped his sons with the post office and responded to issues as justice of the peace as needed. Evidently, Richard did not anticipate that his eldest would use his time off to resume his old patterns. Junius had established routines he'd become partial to and began taking advantage of the opportunities to hightail it out of there, either back to Little Rock or elsewhere, on the weekends to have a life!"

I found myself shaking my head in amazement and couldn't help but smile at this latest piece of the story. At my age then, I could still relate to really needing a break from work.

"The long and short of it is that it does not appear the family could make a go of it in Tatumville. I know that at some point, just a couple of years in, they made the decision to shutter the store. Evidently, it wasn't worth their time to stand there all day for the few customers they were seeing."

"That must have been a tough decision."

"They had a bunch of tough decisions to face," she replied. "I'm afraid what started out as an attempt to do the right thing for his sons backfired on Richard in a cascading manner."

"Backfired in a cascading manner? What are you trying to say?" I asked her point-blank, my left eyebrow askew.

"Junius had picked up his carousing behavior right about where he'd left off and was soon getting into trouble all over again. It all must have been too much for his mother," Aunt Joni concluded with a pause.

"What happened?"

"I can't say exactly. From what I've already shared and from what I've yet to disclose, I can tell you that a lifetime of loss, heartache, stress, and hard work may have gotten the better of her. By the twelfth of February 1888, she'd passed on. Richard included in his notes for the family Bible that his wife, the mother of their children, was buried in lot sixty-three at the Mount Holly Cemetery in Little Rock."

"How long did she live?" I asked.

"She would have been fifty-six years old that June. Richard hardly had a couple of months to mourn." Her voice trailed off with the suggestion of something left unsaid.

"What? What happened?"

"I think I'd better fill in a little more detail. I know I mentioned there was no money down on the property deal with Tatum."

"Yep, you did."

"Did I mention they missed their first annual payment for April of 1887?"

"No," I responded almost accusingly. "You left that part out!"

"My apologies. You are correct. Cornelia died two months before they missed the second payment in April of 1888. What they had saved for that payment may have been spent on her funeral and burial. And Cornelia managed to miss her daughter's wedding. Late that summer, Richard married off their daughter Cornelia. Remember Nellie?"

"Yeah. How old was she when she married?"

"She married Sanford Goodwin that August at the ripe old age of twenty-four!"

"Okay. Wasn't there something else that went with this part?"

"Yep, there are several more something elses to this part. Help me stay on track!" She laughed.

I wasn't sure how to respond to that. I knew she was on track for something, but I had no clue which track we were on! The sound of my aunt's voice brought my focus back.

"I've got to backtrack to before Nellie's wedding, but I didn't want to forget it. Not long after the second payment was missed, Mr. Tatum filed an action at law in Saline County court against Richard, and Richard lost the lawsuit."

"No kidding? Just like that? What happened?"

"On the tenth day of April 1888, the court found for Tatum and ordered a judgment against the land and the building. It was posted to be sold at auction and then was sold to the highest bidder the following month, on May 26th. Tatum also managed to convince the court to seize the mules and wagon."

"So, two months after Cornelia dies, they've lost their home, their land, and their wheels in one fell swoop?" I was pretty sure I'd tracked it all, but they really did appear to have a cascading waterfall of trouble on their hands.

"Not exactly," was her curious reply.

"I don't get it!" I exclaimed. "You lost me again. What happened?" It seemed our family stories all had a curious similarity. They would lead me off in one direction, only to land me somewhere else. It had the effect of forcing me to pay even closer attention so I didn't miss anything.

"According to his legal deposition to the court, a man by the name of Mr. Bush, who referred to himself as the local druggist

– a pharmacist, we'd call him these days – stepped up to buy the property at the auction."

"Okay," I replied, trying to maintain my patience. "So, how does that translate into them not losing their place?"

"Here's what I know. Prior to the auction, a man by the name of Mr. A.D. Jones approached our druggist, Mr. Fred Bush, and whispered in his ear, as they say."

I could hear the plot thickening but had no idea what to expect she'd say next. I did know that with my family, just about anything was possible. "So, what did he whisper, and how could you possibly know all of this?" I finally asked and demanded simultaneously.

"According to Fred Bush, Mr. Jones told him he could help Mr. Whitmore and, if it didn't work out, he'd have the place to make a go of it for himself. He couldn't lose if he bought their place at auction."

"You're kidding, right?" I replied, stunned at this news.

"Fred Bush acknowledged to the court he'd already made a deal to sell the spread to Junius for the same price – if he were to win the auction."

"Was that legal?" I asked, still half mind-boggled. Aunt Joni scrunched her eyebrows and grimaced before she continued.

"Not long after that, Richard filed what he referred to as an attachment lawsuit on Junius's behalf against Tatum – which Junius won, recovering his mules, the wagon, and sixty-six dollars in damages for lost wages."

At this point, I was shaking my head; my eyebrows were raised, and my mouth was hanging open. But I had to press my point. "You still didn't answer me, Aunt Joni – how could you possibly know this much detail about all of this. It's like you were there!"

Joni chuckled. "It's because I have access to their actual written and verbal testimonies reflecting back on what happened during a legal action that hasn't happened yet in our tale."

Holy shit, Sherlock! Her sleuthing had me floored again. With that, we took a break.

* * *

"Okay," Aunt Joni said after my shock had settled. "So, remember I was starting to tell you that Richard hardly had a year to mourn his wife's passing when, the next thing he knew, your great-great-grandfather Junius Brown had got himself into really deep hot water?"

"Was it about the property? Was that it? Or was there something else?" I pressed her. When she continued to silently stare at me, I knew it had to be something else. "Uh-oh. I can only imagine! What did he do now?"

"He'd sown too many wild oats!" she exclaimed.

"I understand how that might happen," I added with chagrin. We both laughed at that.

"And then, on March 4, 1889, Benjamin Harrison, the grandson of our ninth president, William Harrison, was sworn in as the twenty-third president. Six new states joined the Union during his term. He was known as a man of integrity, but his efforts to reform civil and voting rights laws were stymied by an uncooperative Senate. Historians suggest little progress was made on the civil rights front for the next several decades."

"How many presidents later was that?" I asked with just a hint of cynicism.

"Way too many!" my aunt replied.

"Well, that sure explains quite a bit about where we are now."

"While Harrison defeated President Cleveland in 1888, he then lost to him four years later. I was amazed to see that there were more than five million votes cast in the 1892 election. The Harrison presidents were the only grandfather-grandson duo ever elected, and Cleveland was the only president thus far who was elected for two non-consecutive terms."

"That's fascinating, Aunt Joni; however, I wouldn't be doing my job if I didn't remind you that you've left Junius dangling in the wind with all of your presidential pussyfooting," I interjected, unable to resist teasing her to see if I could throw her off track.

"Thank you for bringing me full circle. So, literally within a day or two of Benjamin Harrison's presidential inauguration, Richard received a visit from a contingent of Cherokee elders. While that wasn't so unusual, it became clear pretty quickly that this was no ordinary visit."

"What did they want?" I asked her.

"They wanted Richard to get his son to do right by one of their daughters. Evidently, J.B. had begun to make a practice of visiting her and had been spied leaving her place early one morning. The elders knew it was only a matter of time before children followed. Richard was known to them in Saline County as an attorney and justice of the peace, and they may have known he would at least listen to their request with the gravity it deserved."

"What was their request?" I asked, beginning to get the picture.

"They wanted Junius Brown to marry and provide for her. It would have been a hardship for the woman to care for a child on her own. Even now, it remains a hardship for single parents to cope with raising children alone."

"Wow! So, what happened?" I asked as she paused to take a drink of water.

"Richard wholeheartedly agreed. His son was an adult and would be held accountable for his behavior. He locked up the post office and took the group of elders upstairs to find J.B. I can only imagine the look on your great-great-grandfather's face as they all walked in to face him. He must have gotten a pretty quick clue as to what might be coming!"

Once again, I found myself wide-eyed and speechless.

"They left Junius little choice. The wedding would take place the following week, before J.B. might have a chance to change his mind. On March 10, 1889, Junius married your great-great-grandmother, Susan Edith Ferguson Whitmore Tinkle."

"Oh, my God! That's another wow! Dad once told me we were part Cherokee, but I never knew what happened!"

"I shudder to imagine my great-grandmother Susan's extended family story, frankly. This one hit close to home five ways to Sunday. Her ancestors appear to have trod the roughly eight-hundred-mile Trail of Tears from eastern Tennessee all the way out to Oklahoma, which I mentioned earlier."

My hand almost instinctively moved to my forehead as I began to realize the weirdly synchronistic connections in the historical developments of the families.

★ ★ ★

I must now interrupt my long-ago conversation with my aunt for just a minute to address my patient audience. These synchronicities continued to play out for us in real time while we were recording the audio version of the first volume of *Torch Time Tales*.

"What do you mean? Say more!" one of the members of the audience offered to everyone's laughter.

I'll add that this wasn't the first synchronicity to occur that paralleled our efforts.

On July 9, 2020, while our producer was recording the audio for chapter two, in which my aunt introduced the subject of the 1830 Indian Removal Act and the Trail of Tears, it was announced that the United States Supreme Court had used a rape case to finally overturn nearly two hundred years of congressional inaction on a long-forgotten promise made by the US government to those same tribes they had forcibly moved – that they could have the land in Oklahoma in perpetuity.

The Supreme Court launched what will be a long federal process of returning a good portion of the state of Oklahoma back to the descendants of the Native Americans from Tennessee and elsewhere that were marched there.

So, with that parallel synchronicity now noted, let me allow Aunt Joni to finish her train of thought.

★ ★ ★

"Do you remember me mentioning the Indian Removal Act of 1830 a few nights ago?" She asked me. I nodded and sighed. This time, however, I had a pretty clear idea of where she was heading next.

"The US government used the Cherokees' last easternmost capital of Red Clay, Tennessee, to assemble them all in 1838 before ordering the military to forcibly relocate them to Oklahoma, where they would purportedly be out of the way of the legions of oncoming European settlers. Historians estimate that as many as four thousand Cherokee lost their lives on that brutal trip. Red Clay is approximately three hundred miles due east of Grand Junction, Tennessee. As I'd mentioned, the relocation march with Susan's ancestors may very well have passed near Burwell's expanding plantation in the southwest corner of that state."

I sat there and shook my head at her in amazement.

"Susan Edith Ferguson was born in 1869, about thirty years after the Trail of Tears, in an area that, years later, would be named Shawnee, Oklahoma, after the original inhabitants. Historians suggest there was increasing pressure among the transplanted native peoples who were living there to assimilate, as the land was divvied up by white Christian settlers. Sometime not long after her birth, her family moved to Arkansas. I was surprised to learn some of the Cherokee who eventually came to live in southern Arkansas held slaves themselves."

"Wow! I had no idea," was all I could find to say in response.

"When I went back to look at the records, both the Saline County handwritten marriage license application and the printed marriage record listed Susan as twenty-one years old. Based on her birth date, and assuming that's correct, at the point Susan was married to Junius, she was actually not quite twenty years old."

"I don't understand. Why the difference in her age?"

"I don't know. It may have had something to do with appearances. He was substantially older than she was at that point. I can tell you that Junius's marriage to Susan turned out to be the tip of the iceberg for him," she said softly.

"What do you mean?" I asked, exasperated.

"That kind of news spread like wildfire in a small town, even more so when it involved the likes of well-known people like Richard and his family. Plans for the wedding had been kept quiet, but once the deed was done, word spread quickly and eventually fell upon the ears of another woman in the community, who was quite upset to hear the news."

Aunt Joni paused to look squarely into my eyes. I must have had a strange look on my face.

"Are you okay?" she asked me.

"Yes, please go on," I encouraged her.

"The very next day after the wedding, on March 11, 1890, Richard Augustus was back working in the post office when the door opened and in came two men he knew by sight. Richard greeted them and collected up mail that had arrived for the local magistrate, who also lived in the area. The magistrate thanked him, and then he and the local constable sat down. They looked uncomfortable, and Richard suspected something was up. The men had gotten to know one another in Richard's capacity as justice of the peace. The town just wasn't that big."

"So, what was up"? I couldn't help but ask. "Why'd they go see him?"

"There was an awkward pause between them," she went on. "The magistrate finally shook his head and, with a grimace, reached into his inside coat pocket and pulled out the paperwork. It was a summons for J.B.'s arrest. As justice of the peace, it was part of Richard's job to serve them on the unfortunate recipients."

"Why did they want to arrest Junius Brown?" I asked in shocked disbelief. "Was it about the property?" Aunt Joni had not answered when I'd asked her the first time.

"Richard unfolded the paperwork and began to review it. Upon hearing of J.B.'s wedding that morning, a local woman by the name of Mary Theme had come forward and made the complaint. J.B. was charged with bastardy."

"Bastardy?" I'd never heard of such a charge.

"The woman was pregnant and claimed J.B. was the father. Given that he'd been married to Susan the day before, Mary Theme's child would have been considered a bastard."

"Oh. Okay, I get it!" I replied, still dumbfounded. I'd never known there'd been such a legal charge.

"After reading the complaint, which must have been somewhat of a shock, Richard looked up to see his friends staring with eyebrows raised and knew what he had to do. Without a word, he gathered his keys and locked the door to the post office behind them. The three men walked next door. They opened the door and walked inside, and for the second time in the space of a week, J.B. caught one look at his father's face and had to know more trouble was ahead."

"'Son,' he said, 'I have in my hands a complaint that's been filed against you this morning, and these men are here to place you under arrest.'"

"Wow! What did Junius say to that?"

"What could he say? His world was crashing around him. He had now succeeded in doubly disgracing himself. And Richard, who was charged with upholding the law, had no choice but to watch as his son was hauled off to jail."

"Unbelievable!" I announced. I found myself squarely in Junius's shoes, imagining my own head spinning between making one woman's day to totally pissing off another in the span of forty-eight hours or so. "So, what happened? And how do you know all this? It's like you were there!"

Aunt Joni reached over and picked up a folder. "We have copies of the handwritten documents from this case." She opened the file. "I found a copy of an article about Richard Augustus in our family Bible when I was a youngster, I think I mentioned. I remembered it and made our cousin Paula a copy as she began to try to identify her immediate relations. She researched the court documents that allowed us to add this particular piece of the puzzle together."

"So, what happened to Junius?"

"Richard decided to let Junius spend that night in jail. Perhaps he wanted to make sure Junius would be forced to ponder the seriousness of the charges. He didn't post bail for him until the following day, March 12th. I'll read from the record if you like."

I nodded in reply, spellbound by the story.

J.B. Whitmore being in Custody charged with the offense of bastardy in Saline County permitted to give bail in the sum of $200 two hundred dollars for his Appearance before A.A. Crawford, County Judge of Saline County, to answer the Complaint made by Mary Theme.

We the undersigned residents of Saline County hereby undertake that the above named J.B. Whitmore shall appear before the Judge of the County Court of Saline at the Court house in Benton on the 14th day of March 1889 at 10 o'clock AM to answer said Charge & shall at all times render himself amenable to the orders & process of said court in the prosecution of said charge & if convicted shall surrender himself in execution thereof or if he fails to perform either of these conditions that we will pay to the State of Arkansas the sum of $200 given under our hand and seal this March 12, 1889.

My aunt handed me a copy of the record to examine. "It's signed by two men here at the bottom," she pointed out, "with their seals – they must have been clerks of the court."

I read through the page. "This is amazing. How embarrassing for Richard! Two hundred dollars was a lot of money in those days, wasn't it?"

"It was a fortune. And I bet you can guess who had to come up with it!"

"Great-great-great-grandfather Richard," I replied, having fun tripping my tongue over his greatness.

"That's right! It was an expensive month. Richard had to eat the cost of a shotgun wedding and a bail bond, all on his son's account, in short-order fashion! And did you catch that the residents of

Saline County were on the hook for making sure he appeared again in court?"

"I wondered about that."

"These were public documents in a legally binding process that was meant to maintain law and order in those days," she explained. "There were expectations that laws would be upheld and order would be maintained. Richard had been a practicing lawyer for years – he of all people understood that Junius had to be brought to account."

"What happened then?" I asked.

"The next document was from his March 14th court date," she said, pulling another sheet of paper out of the file. "It's a bit hard to make out, but I'll read it to you if you like."

"Yes, please," I replied.

"This one is entitled 'State of Arkansas v. J.B. Whitmore – Bail Bond.'"

"I don't understand. I thought he already posted bail," I interrupted, confused.

"He did. This second one was written after his initial court date," she noted, and then she began reading from the page:

J.B. Whitmore being in Custody Charged with the offense of Bastardy and having been arrested and brought before me as County Judge; and it appearing that the plaintiff or complainant in the action will not be delivered of said bastard Child until sometime in the month of October A D 1889, the Defendant is permitted to give bail in the sum of one hundred and fifty dollars, and we R.A. Whitmore, and the Honorable M.K. Movbly of the County of Saline and the State of Arkansas hereby undertake that the above named J.B. Whitmore shall appear before me at my office in the Town of Benton, County of Saline and State of Arkansas on the 7th day of October A D 1889 this being the regular time of the October

Saline County Court to answer Said Charge and shall at all times render himself amenable to the order and process of this same Court in the prosecution of said Charge and if Convicted Shall surrender himself in execution thereof and if he fail to perform either of these conditions that we will pay to the State of Arkansas the sum of one hundred fifty dollars.

"And see here," she said, pointing to the bottom of the page. "It's signed by the judge and Richard Augustus Whitmore!"

"I don't get it. Why was the bail bond done twice?" I asked, shaking my head.

"The responsibility for Junius Brown's future appearance before the court was officially transferred from the residents of Saline County on behalf of Mary Theme, who'd made the complaint, to Richard and the county judge," my aunt clarified. She paused to take a sip of water before continuing.

"I'm sorry, Aunt Joni. I'm still not getting it."

"I spent a while looking at this. From the way it was drafted, I'd say Richard and the judge were well acquainted. Richard himself may have drafted the document for the judge to sign. And I have to point out that in the process, he must have gotten his colleague to agree that two hundred dollars bail was a bit stiff. Did you catch that bail was reduced to 150 dollars in this second bond?"

"That's right!" I exclaimed. "Was that right that they did that?"

"It was within the purview of the judge. And remember, Richard Augustus was known to the court. He was, in a sense, with this bond, putting his own reputation at stake and on the line that his son would show up when ordered to do so later that fall."

"And did he?" I wanted to know.

"Yes, he did," she answered, pulling the last legal papers from the file. "These are the hardest to decipher, so bear with me. The first part restates what happened – to enter it formally into the record, I presume. See if you can catch the change they made."

"No problem!"

State of Arkansas v. J.B. Whitmore – before the County Judge March 11th 1889. Upon the 11th day of March 1889 upon complaint of Mary Theme a certain woman resident in the County of Saline that she is pregnant with child which if born alive will be a Bastard whereof she attests the defendant J.B. Whitmore to be the Father. A warrant is issued to the constable of Beaver Township commanding him forthwith to bring before me the defendant J.B. Whitmore to answer said complaint and on the 12th day of March 1889 came the defendant J.B. Whitmore in custody of said constable. Whereupon it is ordered that defendant J.B. Whitmore enter into bond to the State of Arkansas in the sum of $200 for his appearance as Required by law. Whereupon John Lindsey and Galen H. Movbly assuring his security and are acknowledged by said Court as sufficient to enter in to such Bond, the defendant J.B. Whitmore was discharged until further orders herein – and on this the 23rd day of October 1889 comes J.B. Whitmore the Defendant in this cause and Mary Theme the mother of the Bastard Child which was born on the 8th day of October 1889. Whereupon it having been proven that said child had been born and the Defendant having entered his plea of Guilty as being the Father of said Bastard Child: It is therefore ordered that the defendant J.B. Whitmore with good and sufficient Security enter into a Joint penal obligation in the sum of $800 conditioned according to law. Whereupon the defendant, his security deemed by the Court as sufficient enters into such obligation and it is thereupon ordered and considered just punishment.

"Unbelievable!" It was all I could muster in the moment.

"It goes on to list all the expenses related to his arrest and the case. He was ordered to pay back everybody involved for expenses incurred on his behalf, and it spelled out that he was required to make monthly child support and alimony payments to Mary Theme and her child for as long as the child should live until he reached adulthood. And that he would not be dismissed from the obligation until the boy either became an adult or was no longer living, as acknowledged by the court."

"They changed the amount of the bail bond again, didn't they?" I asked.

Aunt Joni laughed out loud. "You caught that, did you? The judge had to make the record agree with the facts! He evidently decided to omit the part where he and Richard agreed to cut a separate deal after the original bond had been issued. And it took me a while to see it, but it's clear to me now why Junius is only identified by his initials in every last one of these proceedings. Richard Augustus may very well have used his position to shield his son – and the family's privacy and reputation in the process – recognizing, over time, it might be more difficult to determine exactly who 'J.B.' might have been. Fascinating, huh?"

"All of it. It's unfucking believable! But is there more to this part of the tale?" I asked her a bit anxiously.

"There is more – but how about we pick up at this point tomorrow evening?" she inquired, beginning to get her muscles in motion.

"Okay," I agreed begrudgingly.

CHAPTER 7

Bucking the Tide

We both slept later than usual the following morning. I made myself a cup of coffee and stepped outside to join Joni on the veranda. "Good morning!" I offered up as I sat down on one of the chairs.

"Good morning," she replied with a smile.

I noticed Joni raise her arm and point beyond the pond toward the blue and white golf tees back behind the line of giant oak trees. There were three deer, a mother and two tiny newborns. "Those two fawns – they're so precious!" I exclaimed, delighted to have such a sight to start my day.

"They make a circuit in the community over a twenty-four period. The best shade spots around are well known and staked out early by those in the know," she added, still smiling. "That undeveloped grassy area there behind the oaks is one of the nursery spots where they bed down at night. The fawns get trained to return there when they get separated from their mothers."

"That's fascinating! You're almost implying they're educating one another."

No sooner had I finished my sentence than the two fawns began a highly charged, playful dance. As they pranced, ran, jumped, and twisted, every possible move their little bodies might conceive was displayed back and forth for one another – to their amusement and our own. Their mother continued eating, seemingly oblivious to their antics as they raced from one side of the fairway to the other.

"They aren't the only ones," she replied. "I've watched the ducks lead synchronized swimming exercises with their little ones all in a line, drilling them to swim back and forth, ducking and diving together, then adding short bursts of flight that cascade into simultaneous sliding stops across the water, only to watch them turn around to repeat the exercises again and again."

"Really?" I asked, not because I doubted what she was saying but to express my amazement. Obviously, I had not spent as much time with nature as my aunt had over her lifetime.

"A British scientist by the name of Rupert Sheldrake coined the term 'morphic resonance' to describe how species learn from one another over time. It's been well researched by scientists. Didn't I mention the geese?"

"Rupert Sheldrake? His name rings a bell. I'm not sure if I've heard about morphic resonance or not. That's a mouthful! And what about the geese?"

"Once we realized they were laying eggs up in the craw of the old willow, we noticed that the female of the primary pair of residents would periodically have small groups of other geese with her at the base of the tree, where she would demonstrate for them how to approach the fly-up between the large branches to access the spot for nesting."

"You're not kidding, are you?" I asked her rhetorically.

Joni smiled. "If it had only happened once, I might have written it off as a fluke. One year, the female was able to hatch a brood of eight goslings. As soon as they were able, the pair of parents began a daily habit of marching those little ones all the way around the pond to build their leg muscles and their appetites!"

"That's amazing. Being here gives me a whole new perspective. This is going to sound strange, but I can almost feel my brain expanding. What are you doing to me, Aunt Joni?"

"I'm working your butt off!" she replied sarcastically.

We both laughed at that. There was some truth in her statement. It was my mind, however, that was really feeling the exercise. Maybe my body was just more used to a workout. I don't know. All these years later, I'm still processing everything I absorbed. One thing I noticed almost immediately after being there with her was that my appetite increased like crazy! Joni tried to explain to me that the mind, when engaged, has the capacity to use even more calories than the body. That was a hard one for me to swallow, but my stomach was clearly in agreement.

* * *

"So, after Junius married Susan and after he was released from jail on bond in the bastardy case, the two of them lived together as husband and wife. That same summer, they conceived a child," Aunt Joni began that evening, as promised.

"She must have forgiven him," I offered.

"Perhaps," Joni replied. "She was legally his wife – we know that much, although their marriage license was very difficult to decipher. When the Saline County marriage license, which I mentioned earlier, was eventually transcribed and published, it listed James B. Whitmore of Tatumville as the man who married Susan Ferguson. All other details of the matrimony, the day, the year, the place, their ages – he was listed as thirty-six; she was listed as twenty-one – everything else matched." She shook her head in disbelief but held off speaking.

"What? What were you going to say?" I pressed her.

"I'm struck by the fact that records were left such that it was James B. Whitmore who married Susan and J.B. Whitmore who was charged with bastardy. I suspect confusion around his identity shielded Junius Brown Whitmore and his father somewhat from the embarrassment of the full brunt of public opinion on all counts."

"Wow!" I replied, totally stunned at the latest revelations. "He pulled a Burwell, didn't he? This is amazing! How could one guy get into so much trouble?"

"That is a very important question," she agreed, laughing with me. "That fall, the verdict was delivered in his bastardy case. Beyond that point, I don't know what happened to J.B.'s bastard child."

Joni had preempted the very question I was going to ask her next.

"I do know that on February 21, 1890, your great-grandfather Murphy was born," she continued. "And don't ask me quite yet how, but I also know firsthand from Sheriff Shoppach, who had been in that position there for the past eight years, that Junius moved out of the post office that same month. Given the timing of Murphy's birth, he may have moved out of his place with his father and brothers at the P.O. to be with his wife someplace else – probably someplace with more privacy prior to Murphy's birth."

"It's weird to get my head around all of this, I have to tell you. So, really what you're telling me is that there's a whole line of Whitmores out there in the world that aren't named Whitmore anymore. Do you suppose that these kids of Junius looked enough alike that they might have been able to recognize one another as they grew up?" I pondered the shock I would feel if I passed someone walking on the street and immediately recognized myself in a total stranger.

"It is in the realm of possibility that Mary Theme did give her child Junius Whitmore's name. Junius pled guilty, you might recall, and legally acknowledged his paternity. At one point, when your brother was doing his breathtaking research, we were talking on the phone, and he told me about a Junius Whitmore that showed up in the census in Little Rock years later, after our Junius had passed on. At that moment, I didn't make the connection to this possibility. Neither of us has yet had a chance to further research the question."

"Wow, that's a mind-blowing new possibility, Aunt Joni. I wonder how many Junius Whitmores could have lived in that same or subsequent years with his name who weren't related to him? I mean, come on. Junius just isn't that common a first name, is it?"

"We are talking about the south," she replied. "When I reread the bastardy case, however, it does appear the court was attempting to shield the sex of the child. So, it's also possible Mary Theme's bastard child was a girl. Still, you make a strong point, and so as not to lose your prior point, it is quite possible Junius's half-brothers or sisters could have recognized one another or that they even knew one another. Even if they weren't recognizable, they may have been made aware of one another by their respective family members. It's not clear that any of them would have maintained confidentiality."

"What a bizarre mystery," I interjected.

"At some point, DNA will help future generations that want to figure it out," she added. "I'd love to be able to meet them!"

I knew where Aunt Joni was going with this one. I imagined putting in an order to serve up the names of my relations descended from Junius Brown Whitmore's bastard child. For all I knew, some of them might live right down the street, or perhaps I'd already met one of them and didn't even know it.

"Literally four days after Murphy Whitmore was born, J.W. Tatum started up his legal engines again."

"Huh? What happened?" I asked her, starting to get disoriented all over again.

"On February 25th, 1890, he had his attorneys file an amended complaint to his original one with the court. Then his attorneys began taking depositions among the various parties that were involved. The foreclosure lawsuit named Richard, his son Junius, and Fred Bush as defendants. Tatum accused the three of them of fraud and collusion in the whole deal."

When she'd finished, my aunt looked over to see the lightbulbs going off for me as I had my "Oh, wow" moment. "Four days apart, huh? That's wild! There wasn't a dull moment in that family!"

"As the various parts of this portion of the *Tales* came together, I had to do some serious head-scratching and reformulating to line up all these closely interrelated dates. So, now you know the original source materials to which I've been privy. The written depositions were filed with the case, and one of Tatum's attorneys also cross-examined the available witnesses."

"Unbelievable! Wait a minute, Aunt Joni." By this point, I was getting hip to the various clues she would interject from time to time – used to monitor how closely I was paying attention, I'm sure. "What were you trying to imply when you said they cross-examined the available witnesses?"

"I learned quite a bit more about what happened in our situation from who wasn't there and what wasn't said!" she exclaimed.

"Oh?" I asked, looking at her askance. Sometimes this would be just enough to keep her expanding on whatever she'd been talking about that little bit longer.

"Let me put it this way. Although named in the lawsuits, Junius Brown Whitmore appears to be missing in action, by and large, although he and his father jointly filed their response to Tatum's amended complaint. After that point, however, he was not deposed himself and was seemingly not available for cross-examination. His father, Richard, testified his son lived with him for most of his life yet completely failed to mention that the man, in the last six months, had two children born to him by two different women and was sued by the one who was not his legal wife!"

"Aunt Joni, please help me understand this. What was really happening here? Why wasn't he deposed? Why wouldn't he have been available for cross-examination?"

"Had the truth come out about Junius and the two women, it would have reflected badly on his character. He was being charged with fraud and collusion. His integrity was on the line as it was, and his actions had further cast a shadow on his father's integrity as he covered for him. It appears to me that Junius intentionally disappeared with his new wife and baby, not to be found and thus not to be served, deposed, or otherwise cross-examined."

"This story is crazy!" I said to her with my mouth still open wide.

"This was after there had already been two court actions that had played out about Tatum's property. Richard argued he'd lost the land outright when it had been auctioned after the 1888 lawsuit. Fred Bush, who amended his original deposition, testified he'd made the deal to help Junius, not Richard, and that Junius had paid him for the property, the same price Fred had paid at auction, less the fifty dollars he allowed Junius to borrow back from him to mortgage one of his mules."

"I'm sure you couldn't have made all this up. I mean, how ridiculous!" I added, laughing. "So, what happened? Is there more to their legal battle?"

"Oh, yeah," she replied. "There were other testimonies, depositions, and documents – several of each. Suffice it to say, the court ruled against father and son, but not completely."

"What?" I exclaimed.

"The court allowed them a very narrow window of time to come up with the rest of the missed payments. Failing that, they would be forever barred from any ties to the property."

"Wow! With the evidence you present, that seems way more than fair! So, what happened?"

"Richard immediately requested the court to consider allowing an appeal on Junius's behalf, which, the record reflects, they granted. The entire case was filed as of May 20, 1890. Murphy would have been just a few months old that June, when Junius and Susan conceived one more son, whom they named Carlyle. He was born the following February, in 1891."

There was a long pause as my aunt sipped her beverage and allowed me time to digest the latest information. When no questions were forthcoming, she continued. "Within five months of Carlyle's birth, Junius Brown Whitmore was dead at the age of thirty-nine. His death left Susan with an infant and toddler to parent alone and allowed him a way to skip out on the child support and alimony responsibilities he had to Mary Theme and their child."

"Geez, Joni, that's incredible!" I exclaimed. "Do we know how he died or what happened to the children? And what happened to his father, Richard Augustus?"

"Junius's life did not end neatly, it's fair to say. The sum of his actions had left him indebted for the rest of his life to his father, with his own obligations outstanding. It may have taken his father some time to get over his disappointment in his son – if he was even able to forgive him. We'll never know."

"Humph! What do you think?"

"It is possible Junius drank himself to death. He was dead two and a half years after he was brought up on the bastardy charge and must have faced some public scorn and humiliation for all of his questionable actions. It's also possible he teed off Tatum or somebody else so badly they killed him or had him killed. As you'll soon be able to gather for yourself, however, his actions had ramifications for his own descendants for generations to come." She paused for a moment, hesitating to say more.

"What were you going to say?" I prompted her.

"Richard and one of his younger sons, Joseph, evidently made some effort over their remaining years to support both of Junius's families. They appeared to understand what it meant to take responsibility for one's behavior. Your great-great-great-grandfather Richard Augustus Whitmore lived to see the turn of the century. He would have been alive to see William McKinley elected the twenty-fifth president of the United States in 1897."

"Isn't Mt. McKinley the tallest mountain in North America?" I asked her, already knowing the answer.

"Yes, and thankfully, her name has been restored to Mt. Denali, an ancient name for the Great One, by some of our Alaska Native relations. McKinley the man was the last president to have served in the Civil War. His term ended when he was assassinated in 1901, which made way for our twenty-sixth president, Teddy Roosevelt, rated by scholars as one of the five best presidents ever."

"So, when did Richard die?" I asked, now confused from the sidetrack we'd made.

"Richard Augustus Whitmore's story ended in March of 1900. He was seventy-seven years old and left many descendants. His three grandchildren from Junius Brown – the two sons he had with Susan and his child with Mary Theme – would have been about nine and ten years old when Richard passed on. At that point, from what I know, the two mothers and their children were on their own."

"What a story! After all that, I feel like I know my great-great-great-grandfather Richard – or at least, I know a lot more about him than I did before!"

"He must have developed some amount of inner strength," she replied. "To watch so many family members pass on before him – from the time he was a very young boy and continuing throughout his lifetime. Not to mention the atrocities of the Civil War they endured. And yet he continued to carry on."

"It's totally fucking mind-blowing, is what it is!" It was all more than I hoped to ever have to deal with at that point in my own life.

"I have respect for him for choosing a path so different from his father's, and yet that couldn't have been easy, either. To have the strength of conviction to study the law during those difficult times is impressive, especially when the sentiments around civil rights were so confused. He had to be brave and strong to buck that enormous tide along the way."

Joni turned to see me staring into the night. I was speechless.

"Let's give it a rest tonight, eh?" she said abruptly. "We can pick back up tomorrow. And remind me that I've got something I want to show you."

CHAPTER 8

All Eyes to the Horizon

We both slept in late. After fetching ourselves some snacks, we headed outside. The temperature was just about perfect – the air fresh and cool from overnight rain. By this point in our adventure, I had more than a few questions piling up. "You never explained why the family tale-teller is called the torchbearer," I put to her point-blank.

"You've watched a relay race before, haven't you?" she asked me in reply. "It's kind of like that. In this tale, one runner starts out telling the tale, and when they get to the end of their leg, they pass the baton to the next runner, who passes it to the next, and so on. In our family, it's not so much a baton that we're passing on from one generation to the next; it's a torch."

"But why do we use a torch?"

"Have you noticed how the torch here sheds just enough light for us to see one another by?" she asked. "Can you make out the point where the light ends and the darkness begins?"

I nodded. It was plain that I was going to have to let her explain. My aunt was a bit slower these days, my brother had warned – and he had encouraged my patience in advance. She wasn't like working people, constantly rushing around and complaining about not having enough time. There was clearly no rushing Aunt Joni.

"Torches are an ancient symbol of enlightenment," she clarified. "When torches are put in front of us, they can light the way ahead so we can step more sure-footedly. And when put behind us, they shed enough light so we can see and learn from where we've been. However, each is limited to one degree or another. They can only shed so much light at any given point in time in an infinite universe." She paused to allow her words to sink through my thick skull.

"There's more than enough history to be had just from the Whitmore side of the family," she went on, "and if you had preferred, we could have begun this tale more than a thousand years ago!"

"No way!" I'm sure I replied at the time.

"Yes, way!" She laughed.

"How is that possible?" I cried out skeptically.

"Well, I have had help from more directions than I can count," she said, smiling and nodding. "As time progressed, I followed some of the trails back to the original sources as they became available."

"Huh?" I was lost.

"Did you know there's an old family legend?" she asked me with one eyebrow raised.

"Now you're seriously pulling my leg, aren't you?" I said, half smiling and half in shock.

"The legend dates back a thousand years."

"You're telling me there is a thousand-year-old family legend?" I was dumbfounded. "How and when did you discover that?"

"I first came upon it by happenstance as a child."

"What does that mean?"

"Your grandparents kept an enormous family Bible in their living room in Oregon that had passed from my father's Arkansas side of the family. As a very young child, I spent many an hour exploring the two large drawers of the cabinet the Bible sat upon. The drawers were chock full of nineteenth- and twentieth-century photos from both sides of the family. Eventually, my attention was drawn to locks of brown hair sticking out from the ends of the Bible, which had been saved there by my three older sisters after their first haircuts. At some point, I managed to get the enormous book open to look. Inside the Bible was a copy of an old Arkansas newspaper article about Richard Augustus Whitmore." She paused to sip her beverage.

"Seriously, though, a thousand-year-old family legend? That's just crazy! Why hasn't anybody told me any of this?"

"It was this same article about Richard Augustus Whitmore by Virginia Fuller I've mentioned to you a couple of times now that exposed me to the legend for the first time as a youngster. I had never heard about it prior to that point, and I do not ever remember it being discussed among my family. When my cousin Paula called some four decades later, trying to learn the names of our grandparents and other ancestors, I remember telling her I was pretty sure I knew where to look. The article was just where I'd found it decades before."

"And the legend?" I pressed.

My aunt smiled back at me wryly. "There is physical evidence of the Whitmore clan in England dating back before King John's signing the Magna Carta in the year 1215," she replied, ignoring my direct question for the moment.

"Really?" I asked, unbelieving. "How is it possible for you to know that?"

"Well, let's just say for now that the Magna Carta had its own twisted history and the importance of that piece of history to later history is still debated. It is believed to have had some impact on the development of law over time in some places. At that time, however, it didn't help people subservient to kings and barons; these weren't laws or rights for the common person. Hundreds of years later, the Magna Carta was referenced in the development of American law."

Unfortunately for yours truly, I still wasn't picking up on her clues. I shook my head at her in befuddlement.

"As to the physical evidence, Whitmore Hall, in the parish of Staffordshire, England, had been in the family since the eleventh century and was later referenced in the Magna Carta. But the Whitmore name and our direct ancestors go back even farther than that."

"They do? Really?" I could hardly believe her. We were already talking about nearly a thousand years of history. My mind was swimming with hers, trying to stay afloat.

"When I began researching the subject as an adult, I again came upon the family legend, but like much of history, it seems to be conveniently incomplete, and it's time the rest of that story comes out as well," she responded quietly.

"You aren't kidding, are you? There really is a family legend?" I asked, amazed.

"As I first read it described, the legend has it that three brothers of Norman descent traveled south in the eleventh century. The first settled in Sussex, the second in Kent, and the third in

Shropshire. Some contributors surmised they came around the time of the Norman Conquest and eventually arrived at an area with a beautiful white meadow or lake. In our case, what was believed to be the Anglo-Saxon family name Whytemere translates to a white meadow or lake."

"That's so cool."

"The use of last names by individuals purportedly began around the same time, and some claimed the Whitmore surname to be among the oldest from this part of the world. As local populations grew, surnames became more common as people began to use them out of a need to separate and identify one John from another, so to say. Some surnames were derived from an individual's occupation, for example, or as has been suggested in our ancestor's case, a geological trait known to their particular area."

"Wait a minute, Joni. Back way up now," I interjected. "The Normans, really? You can't be serious," I practically pleaded with her. "Help me with my history here, please. Who were they?"

"There is a lot of intertwining European history – in this case, in abbreviated form. Let's just say for now that the Normans were historically directly related to the Norsemen, or 'north men,' as in those from the Scandinavian areas to the north who would eventually become the Norwegians, for example, and who conquered and mixed with areas just south of them that had been historically controlled by the French, English, and Welsh. With some amount of effort, I was able to determine that those Norman relations of ours provide our bridge to the earliest-known ancestor on the Whitmore side, born just before the year 900."

"Who the hell was that?" I asked, curious to see if she could come up with a name.

"He had a few names and titles. Rollo was one of them. He personified what we would think of as a stereotypical Viking. He and his Norse crew spent nearly thirty years raiding the northern French coastline before they could stop him."

"Wow, that's some serious recidivism! How did they stop him?"

"They offered him a peace treaty with extended benefits. He was awarded a large tract of land now known as Normandy, France, in exchange for a promise to use his forces to protect the populations on the coastline."

"Wow! Is that really true?" I swear I could not believe my own ears anymore. We'd been subjected to so much fake news over the internet that my inner skeptic now questioned everything. What else did I know about Normandy? From the depths of my brain came an image of the Allied forces storming the beaches. How could I have forgotten that? Modern media had played it every year on the anniversary of the event from World War II. It was the only thing I knew about Normandy.

"It was Rollo's Norse-Norman great-great-great-grandson William the Conqueror, his uncle, and all their relations who, after arriving, staged an invasion of England from the inside out. There was a battle against several others who, like William, claimed to be the rightful heir to the throne. It wasn't long before William successfully established the House of Normandy, the second house of the English crown. The roughly one-thousand-year-old family legend has been researched by many, apparently, and there does seem to be agreement that, at face value, it appears to be historically supportable. They've found land grants that were made to the family by the House of Normandy, including a recorded deed of property in Norman French, along with the family coat of arms reflecting the English grant to the family."

"I don't know what to say, Aunt Joni. This is beyond mind-blowing!"

My aunt wasn't fazed a bit.

"Our thread continues to weave through documented history with the family name carried on through John, Lord de Whytemere of Shropshire, England, whom we know was made a knight in the thirteenth century. By around 1261, John's son Richard dropped the 'de' for the family name to simplify to Whitmore, one among many variations that evolved over time from the original families."

We looked at one another quietly for a minute. This was a lot of new information, and I hadn't expected it. I remember letting out a big sigh at the scope of it all. "It sounds like you had quite a bit of challenge tracking all of these name changes," I finally observed.

"It's a true statement. I eventually came across some cautions for those attempting research so far back in time. Within these thousand years of history that we're tossing around like spaghetti, English, as a language, had three distinct periods, referred to as 'old English,' 'medieval English,' and eventually, 'modern English.' Critically, I was instructed to be aware that spelling was done phonetically. There was very little that had been standardized. You could have the same name of a place or a person spelled as many different ways as the mind could attempt to sound it out. It was commonplace to see in the historical records as I looked backward – and understandable given written records were relatively new."

"So, seven or eight hundred years later, Burwell was pulling a really old rabbit out of the hat, eh?" I asked her, deciding it couldn't hurt to poke some fun.

"That's right." She laughed with me. "And you're giving me the signal that can pull this around full circle. This particular part of the *Tales* is going to have to stay a mini-historical rewind for now, or I'll get too sidetracked from our current trajectory. However, I will share that scientists in 2021 put the Norsemen in North America one thousand years ago, which is almost thirty years before William invaded England and roughly four hundred years before Christopher Columbus arrived here. Suffice it to say, we now know it was the descendants of all of those Norse-Norman-English Whitmores who began showing back up to stay in North America by around 1630. And it was about 150 years after that, you might recall, that you and I originally started this spin around with Burwell Temple Whitmore's birth in 1789."

I nodded and wondered how in the world she managed to maintain her focus through so many threads of time. My own brain was spinning.

"I remember telling you early on that it didn't matter where we began this tale. Now you get a better sense of why. The synchronistic connections between my own life and these genealogical discoveries still rock me. For you see, I'd never heard anything about our descending from the Normans from my parents while they were alive. They would typically describe our family as 'English' or 'Welsh,' and while they seemed to know that both sides of the family were related to the monarchy, there was no family lore about being descended from the Norse or the Normans." She paused.

"So, what's the big deal?" I blurted out, still oblivious to her point.

"Within a brief span from my rediscovery of the family legend, I was diagnosed with Dupuytren's contraction disease."

"What's that?" I asked.

Aunt Joni held up the palm of her left hand for my inspection.

"Wow, Joni. Didn't that Potter character have one of those scars on his forehead?" And without waiting for her to answer, I continued to rattle on, amazed by this most recent discovery about my aunt: "I thought that stuff was just fiction."

"The Potters are from my father's mother's side of the family," she clarified, eyeing me intensely as if I knew something significant. "Let's just say I have personal physical proof that parts of the ancient family legend are likely true. Notice anything?"

What I had noticed was a faded old scar that spanned from the middle of her palm halfway up her pinky finger. I couldn't help but think it looked like either Zorro had left his mark on my aunt or the surgeon must have been under the influence during her surgery! Instead of a straight line, her scar zigzagged back and forth, back and forth, up through the middle of her pinky. In fact, the more I looked, the more my mind's eye wanted to see it as a snake!

"In the old days, they would have said I had the curse of the Vikings!"

"You're kidding, right?" I asked in shocked disbelief. "First a family legend, and now you're throwing me a family-curse curveball?"

"It was later in life before I learned the term 'Viking' was actually never used during the age of the Norsemen. The term evolved after their era as a way to repackage them – and history itself in the process. More historic spin, I'm afraid." She paused.

"I never knew that." By that point in our adventure, I was beginning to realize that an examination of virtually everything I'd ever learned was probably in order.

"My father had this disease," she went on. "It's genetic. The disease causes tissue mutation. The scar tissue just continues to reproduce until it forms along the entire finger tendon, pulling it further toward the palm of the hand. In its most acute form, it cripples the fingers entirely. Fortunately, it can be corrected surgically. Unfortunately, the scar tissue returns eventually. This is a disease that keeps on giving. Here's the synchronistic payoff. Prior to it being named for Dr. Dupuytrens, who wrote about a corrective surgery to treat it in 1831, it really was called the 'curse of the Vikings'!"

At that point, she took my left hand into her own and pointed to my already-bent pinkie.

"You have it as well, nephew," she offered as she ran her finger over the growing mass of tumor.

I remember being too stunned to respond to her. She had managed to encapsulate hundreds more years of our family history in a heartbeat, make it personal in the process, and bring us full circle to where we'd begun. I began to get a sense of the breadth of this task – and a serious clue to the potential fate of my fingers!

"Anyway, to make a long story short," she said, interrupting my brain spinning on it all, "I will continue to share what I can in the time we have a bit at a time. Then it will be up to you. In the future, you will carry the torch, and you, your brother, and your cousins will be the bearers of our family's *Torch Time Tales*."

Her answers continued to take my breath away, I must admit. I knew at that point that the job she was describing was far beyond me. I also knew I'd be on the losing end of the stick if I tried to argue the point.

"So, what do you think about this adventure of ours so far?" Aunt Joni asked me after we'd finished our supper of snacks.

"It's pretty amazing!" I replied without hesitation. "I had no idea what to expect. My friends were afraid I'd be bored to tears. And now I just wish time would slow down. It's passing too fast – although it did take me a while to go to sleep last night."

"Oh? What kept you up?"

"I was thinking about my great-great-grandmother Susan raising two babies alone. That's a little scary."

"Why so?" she prompted.

"I was imagining myself in her shoes, left to raise two little kids by myself as a single parent, and wondering what I would have done!"

"I think that's normal. There are more lessons in these tales than there are hours in the day. I'd venture that magnificent brain of yours will continue to process all of this even as you sleep. It is a lot to sit with, though, isn't it?"

I nodded and looked out at the last light on the pond – calm now after the storm. "Life is full of danger, isn't it?" I sighed.

"Yes, it is," she responded, giving my hair a toss with her fingers. "And it has more questions than any one of us can answer! If you prefer, we can take a break tonight. Or we can stop this nonsense altogether – at any point – you just name it!"

"No way! I'm having the time of my life!" I added for emphasis.

Aunt Joni laughed at that and then got quiet. "I ought to tell you the *Tales* don't get any easier. If this becomes too much, I want you to tell me, and we'll stop. Okay?"

"I'm not a kid anymore, Aunt Joni." I reminded her, raising an eyebrow. "But after everything you've already shared with me, now you're telling me the *Tales* don't get any easier? What the hell could be next?"

"You have a point there, that's true," she replied. "As for myself, I get to watch a little bit of my mind slip away every day at my advancing age." She laughed. "That takes some getting used to! It's taken me all day to realize I forgot to show you the item in the library this morning that I mentioned last evening. So, before I forget, remind me tomorrow," she replied, poking more fun in her own direction.

"Okay, okay, and now can we get back to the *Tales*?" I agreed, knowing I might also forget.

Joni shifted around in her seat and began to get a faraway look in her eye. By now, I recognized this as a sign that she was focusing again on the *Tales*. It was as if she were transporting us back into the actual time and place the events unfolded.

"It was not an easy time for your great-great-grandmother Susan. She had left her home and community, gotten married, borne two children, and been widowed in the span of a couple of years, and she wasn't a whole lot older than you are now. Her life was completely transformed. And while Richard's support made a difference, it didn't prevent the cruelty she experienced. In the white community, her children were referred to as half-breeds. Community sentiment tended toward Mary Theme, seen by some as the real victim in this case, a white woman impregnated and abandoned by a white man – for a native woman, no less."

"That's awful," I countered.

"While Susan had support from her native family, even within the tribe, it was impossible for her to ignore the jealousy and resentment others displayed. She now had a roof over her head in town, and she was able to come and go between her first family and her new home as she pleased. While she was able to walk in two worlds, as they say, ironically, she didn't fit into either one of them very well."

"What happened to Susan and her children?" I asked.

"There was a ten-year span after Junius died before his father Richard passed on – and that decade was relatively stable for Susan. Richard saw to it personally. He tended to want the company of his adult children and his grandchildren, and he was a gracious host. Susan and the boys always had a standing invitation at Grandpa Richard's house."

"That must have made a difference."

"It must have made some difference, I agree," she replied. "Susan never had to worry about anyone being rude or inconsiderate to her or the children when she was there. Richard wouldn't stand for it. And he shared as much as he could with her in the time that he had, just as his sisters had so importantly done for him. He wanted to provide some level of happiness and stability for her and the boys. Under the circumstances, I suspect he knew it was the least he could do to level the playing field fate had dealt his grandsons." Joni stopped for a moment to sip her soda.

I waited for her to continue. I wanted to know what happened.

"As they say, time marches on. As it was, given that Murphy and Carlyle's father, Junius, died while they were still too young to remember him, Grandpa Richard Augustus played an important part in their lives as a father figure and role model. If only he'd been able to see them through another decade." Her voice trailed off, and again she paused.

"Why do you say that?" I asked.

"They still needed his guiding light," she explained. "Things might have turned out differently. I suspect you'll understand more clearly as the *Tales* unfold. When Richard Augustus Whitmore died, his estate would have been divided among his children or their descendants. Susan might have been left a small sum, but it wouldn't have lasted. Richard, however, had ensured Susan and her sons could read, and he introduced them to the local library, where they were all issued library cards. That proved to be an important resource, and Susan and her boys took advantage of the privilege."

"Wow, times have changed!" I responded. "Who goes to the library anymore? It's all available online, isn't it?" Without waiting for a response, I asked, "So, what happened to Murphy and Carlyle?"

"Their lives got much tougher after Richard Augustus passed. Without his protective shadow cloaking them anymore, Susan was often treated poorly, as just another native and a single mother, no less, with two half-breed boys to feed. Her boys had a hard time staying in school. They were constantly teased and harassed, and eventually, fights would erupt as they defended themselves. Murphy and Carlyle were hardened by their experience. Like their mother, they didn't fit into her native world or the predominantly white world very well. They had to become very tough nuts to survive!"

"So, how did they get by?" I couldn't help but imagine what it would have been like to grow up having people continuously hurl racist insults at me. I'd never had to deal with being put on the spot about the color of my skin. I was aware of my white privilege – a catch-all to describe the rationalization for allowing us all off the hook for our horrific behavior.

"The three of them managed somehow. At some point, Susan remarried. It helped explain our difficulty tracking her ancestry. We were missing her last surname – her second husband's last name. Susan Edith Ferguson Whitmore was buried with the Whitmores in Little Rock as Susan Edith Whitmore Tinkle. Beyond that, I'm clueless about Mr. Tinkle. My father lived with Susan – his grandmother – and had no memory of him."

"There's a wrinkle I didn't see coming," I interjected. "I'm kind of startled to think that Susan lived long enough into the twentieth century for Grandpa Bill to have remembered her."

"Susan eventually had a house in Little Rock. That was huge for them. As a little boy, Murphy loved to watch the red fire trucks race from the fire station to their destination. Richard had given him a toy fire truck for his eighth birthday, a gift Murphy cherished. His grandfather told him that when he grew up, he could land a job at the firehall if he really wanted it. Murphy never forgot that. He brought home every book about firefighters and fire trucks he could find at the library. As he grew older, he worked with a neighboring mechanic to learn how engines and vehicles were put together."

"Interesting. It almost makes it sound like his grandfather planted a seed or two with Murphy that took hold," I observed.

"I agree with you. It wasn't common for Native Americans to know how to read then. They were often segregated from the larger white communities, many of which looked upon them as heathens somehow unworthy of a 'modern' education. Those sent to white schools were often beaten or otherwise abused if they spoke their native tongue – creating the kind of painful scars that last a lifetime, I'm afraid. Murphy didn't make it past the eighth grade before dropping out. He couldn't take the abuse every day, and he didn't see the point. As it was, he spent more time in the principal's office than in class."

"What did Great-grandfather Murphy do then?" I asked, pondering what I might have done if I'd been forced to drop out. I'd never had to consider it.

"Well, Murphy had somewhat of a plan for himself, it appears," she replied. "He hadn't forgotten his grandfather's suggestion for his future. To his surprise, when he approached the fire chief about a job, the man, upon learning Murphy knew some mechanics, could read and follow directions, and already had some amount of work experience, hired him on the spot as part of the clean-up crew. He was told that if he worked hard and showed up on time, they'd keep him on. If he messed up one iota, out the door, he'd go. Their responsibility to the community was too important. While it wasn't much pay, it was a job. Murphy knew that if he kept his head about him,

A Note on Ancestors -- And

By Virginia Fuller

WE KNOW THAT the American Indians took their names from some object, event, landscape feature or even an animal which had some connection with their past or present. But not everyone knows that our ancestors acquired their family names in much the same way.

Whytemere, with its Anglo-Saxon meaning, "White meadow or lake," was the beginning of the name Whitmore, which first appeared in this country about 1640, but now is found from coast to coast. It started in England and the records date back to approximately 1200. John, Lord de Whytemere, lived at Whytemere on the northeast side of Bobbington Parish, in the manor of Claverly in Shropshire, England. He was made a knight in the 13th Century.

During the past 350 years his name has been spelled many different ways. The "de" was dropped about the year 1483, and it since has been changed to Whittemore, Whitemore, Whitimore, Whitmor, Whitmire and Wetmore. Sir Richard, one of the line's descendants, was the first to spell it Whitmore and he chose the simpler version about the year 1495.

There are still many Whitmores in England. Whitmore Hall, located in Salop in the parish of Staffordshire, has been in the family since the signing of the Magna Carta at Runnymede by King John in 1215.

THERE IS A legend that the family is of Norman extraction; that three brothers came to England in the 11th Century, perhaps during the Norman Conquest. One is said to have settled in Sussex, another in Kent and the third in midland Shropshire. This ancient story is substantiated in large land grants, a recorded deed in Norman French, and also in the coat of arms of the family, which included in the crest a lion's head issuing from a ducal cornet—me English grant. The included a falcon, d the outdoors and hu

The Whitmores America have follo

Picture of Richard Whitmore and some of hi

Photo of twentieth-century newspaper article "A Note on Ancestors – And How They Got Their Names" by Virginia Fuller. Includes framed sketch of Richard Augustus Whitmore and some of his marble carvings. Newspaper is unidentified, undated in this xerox copy. This is the article Joni discovers in the family Bible of RAW, from Arkansas, in the Salem, Oregon, house. Most likely published in Arkansas prior to 1961.

eventually, he'd be able to work his way up the ladder, so to speak! And his wages helped put food on the table for his mother and younger brother. He might have been fourteen or so when he was hired."

"No kidding, fourteen? Was it legal for him to work at that age?" I asked in all seriousness.

Aunt Joni couldn't help but chuckle. "Times have changed! I was in elementary school when I was put on a bus to go out to the strawberry fields alone and against my wishes – maybe I was ten years old, if that! It was the expectation that if you were able, you would work. There were few laws outlawing child labor in your great-grandfather Murphy's era."

"Unbelievable!" I remarked, shaking my head. "So, what happened next?"

"Murphy grew up quickly. He was surrounded by older men all day long on the job. Without the civilizing influence of women around, the crews were free to be crude, rude, and as loud as they pleased. As long as their jobs got done, the fire chief let them be. The firemen swapped stories constantly, each trying to outdo the next. Murphy took it all in and got himself an education of another variety." She paused to sip her drink.

"What do you mean?" I asked, not quite understanding.

"There wasn't much they didn't talk about," she replied, smiling. "That was one wild bunch. They traded stories about their trials and tribulations fighting fires, their girlfriends, their sex lives, the latest dirty jokes – you name it, they talked about it. Murphy found himself embarrassed by it all at first. The men left him alone initially, but that didn't last long. Once they found out who his father was, the cat was out of the bag."

"What do you mean, the cat was out of the bag?" I asked.

"It was a small group. It didn't take them long to figure out Murphy's dad was the two-timer who was thrown in jail for knocking up one woman after being forced to marry another! Murphy was dubbed with the nickname 'T.T. Junior,' which eventually was shortened to 'T.T.'"

"T.T. Junior? What did that stand for?" I asked, perplexed.

"They were referencing his father Junius, who'd been a two-timer – he was sleeping with two women unbeknownst to them."

"Oh, I get it. That doesn't sound nice."

"No, it wasn't nice. Murphy took whatever was dished in his direction. He didn't see a choice. Jobs weren't a dime a dozen, and it wouldn't have been any different for him anywhere else, necessarily."

"He must have gotten tough enough to handle that every day."

"Eventually, he grew used to the nickname and even began to feel a little proud of it. At least they liked him enough to call him something other than 'half-breed.' And he was beginning to make friends. He tried to be as useful as possible around the station so they'd want to keep him on board. He couldn't help but feel proud, surrounded by all the fire engines. It was important work."

I thought about the millions of people who'd lost their jobs with COVID-19 in 2020. It brought home for me how much I'd taken for granted in my life – including the jobs I'd landed, held, and ultimately given up to try something different someplace else. The sound of my aunt's voice brought my attention back to our conversation.

"Over the course of the next several years, the firemen came around to accepting him as one of their own. At least, it felt like that to Murphy. He'd finally found someplace he could fit in. He'd earned his right to be there. One evening, after the day shift clocked out, a number of the guys sat down around the breakroom table and began to hash over the week. Murphy was digging in his locker for his lunch pail, getting ready to head home, when one suggested he join them for a couple of shots and a game of cards before they called it a night."

"Did he?" I asked curiously.

"It's not clear he even hesitated. He was thrilled they thought enough to ask him. What harm could come of it? Murphy asked himself. When the others chimed in for him to join them, he couldn't refuse. Soon a chair was located, and space was made around the table for him to sit down. The crew leader reached behind himself to the cupboard and pulled out another shot glass to add to the line-up on the table. One by one, each glass was filled, and the shots were passed around. They raised their glasses, and the crew leader toasted to a job well done."

As I listened, it was as if I was there in the room with Murphy as the scene unfolded before my mind's eye.

"Murphy watched as each man downed his shot in one gulp and put the empty on the table. He stared at the whiskey in front of him and felt the heat from their eyes as they watched to see what he'd do." Joni paused to take a sip. "All this tale-tellin' can make a person downright thirsty," she drawled as best she knew how.

"Wow!" I exclaimed, laughing. "You really sound like a Southerner when you talk like that."

"That's downright generous of you, my dear. Generous," she replied, continuing her drawl.

"So, what did Murphy do?" I asked, trying to get her back on track. "Did he drink the whiskey?"

"He sure did! And then he joined them for another! Can you imagine the ribbing he would have taken otherwise? Remember, Murphy was learning what it meant to be a man. He was going to do whatever they did and then some. That poor boy had already suffered a lifetime's worth of jokes at his expense. He wasn't giving anybody license to give him more grief than he'd already had."

"It was peer pressure," I offered.

"That's right. For Murphy, it was a seemingly important rite of passage. And as far as he was concerned, he'd passed with flying colors. From that day forward, the men included him in their off-duty activities, most of which involved alcohol in one form or another. He never turned down an opportunity to join them, either."

She scooted to the edge of the bench. "And that seems to be as good a spot as any for us to stop for the night."

"Ah, okay," I agreed begrudgingly. "If you must!"

CHAPTER 9

Torchlight Perspective

I woke to the sound of the door opening into my room. I could see Joni's silhouette standing in the doorway.

"Good morning, dear one. I'm sorry to wake you. There's news from up north. It's your dad. I'm getting some coffee going."

I looked over at my phone on the table. I had given myself permission to turn it off after I'd arrived and hadn't missed it. When I powered it up, I found that my inbox was flooded. Then I saw the news from my brother. My dad was in the hospital.

"It sounds like they've got him stabilized," my aunt said to me the moment I sat down for coffee. "He's had a series of strokes." She looked into my eyes and added sadly, "You're going to have to head back north."

"Oh, God," was all I could say.

"I'm so sorry," Joni replied.

"Me, too!" I responded ruefully, feeling my anxiety spike.

My father survived seven strokes. Amazingly, he had no physical paralysis, but the strokes had largely destroyed his short-term memory, leaving him highly vulnerable. It took some time to work out all the arrangements that had to be addressed for him to continue to live at home.

It was months before I would be able to return to see my aunt. As the years passed, I made repeated trips back down to California in just about every season. The respite and revitalization I experienced there with her were unmistakably moving my perspective – on life, the universe, and everything.

* * *

"Shall we pick up where we left off with the *Tales*?" I asked her after dinner the first evening I was able to return to California. Having had time in between to sit with our prior conversations, I was more determined than ever to keep my questions to a minimum.

"Some time ago now, you asked me how a story can have no beginning. Do you remember?"

I nodded, surprised and delighted that she'd come back to the question I'd asked her months before.

"Part of the reason *Torch Time Tales* became a tradition in our family is that, clearly, the lives of the ancestors in our family tree, who lived in different parts of the world at different times over the course of history, are not independent of one another. Multiple generations of relations continue to have an enormous influence on us and those to come."

"I'm beginning to get a sense of that," I agreed.

"Science has helped us see that much of who we are is coded deeply inside us. We've understood for some time that certain physical traits skip some generations – for example, your dad won't go completely bald on top like his dad because the baldness trait is passed from the mother's father. As I was gesturing out toward the universe with my pointer finger earlier, I was reminded of my own mother, who often used this particular gesture. At first blush, you might suppose I learned this behavior from her. In part, that's a true statement."

"That's really fascinating. I had no idea!"

"Science now suggests that our gestures, facial expressions, mannerisms, and much more of what we think of as our own are, in large part, hardwired. These behaviors have been repeated to the point they've left a deep imprint on us and are now part of our ongoing family legacy, although, clearly, science has yet to capture the whole story."

"Wow. You blow my mind, Aunt Joni! What are you going to tell me next?" I added, shaking my head and laughing.

"Well, I will add that by 2013, a team of scientists led by Helen Y. Weng released a study revealing that both the altruistic and selfish actions we take each have an impact on us and our neural responses to suffering; one of them has a positive result, and the other – well, not so much." She paused, reflecting. "That was an enormous breakthrough for science – and the Western mindset. Yet the research wasn't exactly heralded that way at the time. I howled when I read it was nature's way of getting us to work together."

"That's incredible! Where did you find that?"

"I read an online cover article about it, and then, of course, I had to go find the original. The National Institute for Health maintains a National Library of Medicine catalog online that listed the study, which was published by the Association for Psychological Science in their peer-reviewed monthly journal, *Psychological Science*."

"So, are you telling me that on some deep physical level, it really does pay off to be a kind and generous person?"

"And then some!" she responded. "It's easy to see how parents most greatly influence their own children's initial perspective on life, the universe, everything, as they, too, were most influenced by those who came immediately before them. But as our tales reveal, they can't begin to tell the whole story."

"Hmm." I still had to sit with that.

"If you think about it," she went on, "the number of people it took for you to have been born gets larger the farther back you go in history, lessening the mathematical probability that any one relation greatly impacted who you were born to become. So, for example, the three generations prior to your own represent fourteen people! Your mother and father, their parents, and then add their parents – if we stop there, then at least fourteen people made it possible for you to be here!"

"I never thought about it like that," I responded sheepishly.

"And I'd venture to say that over the course of time, the farther back we go in our family history, certain individuals had a far more profound influence on us than others." Aunt Joni paused at this point to take a sip of water.

"But why is that?" I couldn't help but ask.

"Will you save that question? It's a key question, and we'll return to it later. I do want to be clear that the tales I'm sharing with you are relatively true."

I looked at her quizzically, not understanding.

"What I mean is that the stories have unfolded over the course of time. Details have been researched and verified to the extent possible, but given that we weren't present for the full lives of the people involved, there's no telling what's relevant that we haven't been able to learn. It's called an error of omission. And to you, my dear nephew, and to all my relations, I extend my apologies for all such omissions."

"Should you plan to do updated editions if relevant details are discovered?"

"It's a good suggestion. You realize this effort isn't meant to rewrite human history, although time and distance usually do provide us a greater perspective on most everything. If one looks backward and forward in time long enough, one begins to see more clearly. We can begin to get a better sense of these powerful internal drivers, get to know ourselves a little better, and begin to glean a touch of the interrelatedness of it all, even some of the great mysteries of humanity and perhaps the universe itself," she said with a twinkle in her eye.

"I have to say my perspective on our family will never be the same," I responded, smiling and shaking my head at her.

"Long story short, you can see that it doesn't matter where we start the *Tales*. Wherever it is, there was a tale prior to that one, and prior to that one, and prior to that one, all unfolding to set the stage for whichever tale one uses as a starting point. To really get one's head around the wisdom in these tales, to wring out the truths to be known, the more perspective we can glean from each of them to shine upon where we are now, the better!"

"So, it is kind of like a tale within a tale within a tale?" I asked.

"You get the picture! The tales are infinite. To the best of our knowledge, the light that each of our physical lives can potentially shine upon the truths of the infinite universe can only go so far – like our torch over there. The gray area there, between the darkness and the light, that's the fuzzy part, the area that is subject to perspective and interpretation. Of course, the brighter the torch, the more we can see!"

I hardly had time to digest her words before she continued.

"So, where did you and I leave off with the unfolding of the *Tales* the last time you were here?" Aunt Joni asked.

"Murphy!" I declared without hesitation. "You left off with Great-Grandpa Murphy working at the firehouse!"

"That helps boatloads. Thank you," she responded. "Murphy spent some years working at the fire station. He'd grown into a man and hardly had time to notice. It didn't take long before he was riding the engines with the crews and fighting fires with the best of them. It was dangerous, dirty work, and he loved every minute of it. He had found an important role in his community, which brought pride to his mother's house and respect from elders. All this attention was far more to his liking than how he'd been treated growing up. There were stretches when it was quiet, but he still had plenty to do to keep busy at the station."

"That doesn't sound so bad," I commented, remembering her warnings that the *Tales* weren't going to get any easier. "It sounds to me like he was starting to fit in."

"He was fitting in, all right, perhaps a little bit too well."

"Are you planning to say more about that last part?" I asked when she didn't immediately continue.

"You might say he'd fallen into a sideline that suited his situation."

"Huh?"

"When he wasn't working at the firehall, it appears he was keeping busy in the black-market booze business."

"You're shittin' me!"

"No! I'm afraid there's quite a bit more to say on the subject. And as with previous parts of our tales, these chapters have had to be revised more than once as new developments came to light and intersected with what was thought to be true. And like previous examples, here, too, we have a diversion in what was the family version of the tale and what appears to have been the actual one."

"Really?"

"Yes, really! As we get into this, I'm going to try to piece together for you what we knew when."

"Seriously? Wow!"

"It wasn't until the eleventh hour in this decade-plus effort to produce volume one that your brother got a strong calling one day to take another look around for himself and found a trail, courtesy of GenealogyBank and the *Arkansas Gazette*, that Murphy had inadvertently left behind for him."

"This is ringing a bell from something he said to me before I left my dad's, but we didn't have a chance to get into it."

"In March of 1918, Murphy was arrested. He had just turned twenty-eight years old the month before."

"Arrested, huh? What for?"

"He had been found guilty of perjuring himself the year before during testimony he gave May 25, 1917, denying any knowledge of liquor sales in the year prior to that one. In July of 1916, the year the bootlegging took place, he would have been twenty-six years old."

"Wow! Was that the first time he was arrested?"

"It's the first we know of, let me put it that way. Prior to this recent discovery of your brother's, I'd never heard a word about it in my lifetime from anybody. I had no knowledge about Murphy getting arrested. However, from a historical perspective, the timing fits."

"What are you talking about?"

"The Eighteenth Amendment to the US Constitution was passed in 1917. It made it illegal to manufacture, transport, or sell alcohol."

"Prohibition. Of course!"

"It took two more years for the amendment to be ratified by three-quarters of the United States."

"That's fast, though, isn't it?"

"It speaks to how entrenched alcoholism was in this country, how glaring the damage and problems were, that such a consensus developed so rapidly into law. The temperance movement played a large role historically to set the stage. Contrast that speed of adoption with the Equal Rights Amendment, which has yet to be ratified by enough states all these years later."

"That is ironic! And Murphy was making moonshine."

"From what the record reveals, it appears he'd been at it for several years already by that point."

"It sounds like they finally got around to hauling him off to jail!" I replied, thankful I'd never been arrested. "What year was that again?"

"That spring of 1918, he was twenty-eight years old when he ended up spending time in jail for lying about bootlegging. That same fall, he was walking home from work one afternoon when he caught sight of a schoolteacher dismissing her class for the day. She was a pretty, young redhead, and he found himself smiling involuntarily at the sight of her. When she smiled back and waved, he didn't know what to make of it, but it made him curious – and a bit anxious. He resolved to take the same way home again the next day and perhaps catch her eye again."

"Did he?"

"As a matter of fact, he did. He tried to match his timing from the day before, to pass by the school as classes were letting out. And there she was, looking just as beautiful as he remembered. Figuring he had nothing to lose, he summoned his courage, introduced himself to her right there on the spot, and asked her name."

"Was it my great-grandmother-to-be?" I asked.

"It was! Her given name was Anna Pauline Potter. She went by the nickname Billie! She appears to have spearheaded and coordinated one of the first citywide physical education programs in the Little

Rock school system. And my cousin Helen made a point to share that Murphy was strikingly attractive. It's clear he'd caught Billie's eye as well."

"Did he ask her out?"

"There was a dance the following Saturday night, and yes, Billie accepted Murphy's invitation. He was prouder than a peacock to have this fine, educated young woman on his arm, and he did his best to show her off for everyone there to see. They must have had quite a time. That was the beginning of their romance. From that point, Murphy and Billie's courtship blazed like wildfire."

"How could you know that?" I asked her skeptically.

"Remember, they were my grandparents!" she replied and then added, "But sadly, I never met them. To your question, it really was a matter of the dates. The two were married several months later. She was young by today's standards, although not so young for those times. Murphy was twenty-nine, and Billie just nineteen when they conceived their first child, my father. Your grandfather William Junius Whitmore was born the following fall on September 21, 1919."

"Okay, I get it! And they gave him Murphy's dad's name!" I cried in surprise, making the connection.

"Yes, they did! In fact, William was given the names of both his grandfathers; don't forget William Tasville Potter, who was Billie's father, and of course, Junius Brown Whitmore. Murphy wasn't even eighteen months old when his dad passed on. He was too young to remember his father, Junius, but it was a way to honor him for making his life and that of his newborn son possible. Murphy's mother, Susan, may have had something to do with it. Within just a couple of years, they had a second son, whom they named Paul."

"How did they manage if they were both still working?" I asked.

"Good question. It was common for generations of extended families to live together. That's still true in many parts of the world, although less so in modern times in the US until the Great Recession hit. As with the Great Depression, many lost their homes, and with record numbers out of work, families, out of necessity, came together across generations to live like they used to in the good old days."

"Much the same happened with COVID – until the courts began to prevent the evictions," I interjected.

"That's true," she agreed. "When Murphy and Billie got married, the new bride came to live with Murphy at his mother's house. Once the children came along, your great-grandmother Susan watched after her grandchildren, William and Paul, while their parents were at work. Your grandfather William first told me about his grandmother Susan when I was a very little girl – that we had Cherokee blood. My father was one-quarter, I'm an eighth, and you, my precious nephew, are one-sixteenth Cherokee."

Left photo: Murphy Whitmore. Right photo: Anna Pauline "Billie" Potter. I believe these are their wedding portraits, circa 1918-1919, Little Rock, Arkansas (WEC).

"That's just way too cool!" I replied, smiling.

"When I pressed my father to share more about her, he could remember her as an old woman sitting in the kitchen corner. That much, he could call up from his earliest memories as a child. My own attempts to trace her Cherokee history years later hit a dead end. It was a large tribe. Many were inadvertently omitted from tribal registration – and I presumed her identity may have been masked by her marriage into the Whitmore family."

"That's fascinating. What a mystery!"

"One of my father's Arkansas relations from Billie's side disputed the idea that William had a Cherokee grandmother. Certainly not from their side of the family, my cousin Helen insisted. William Junius wasn't honest about more than a few things in his life. We only knew the full story of what happened to him in his last years of life. And yet, as to his grandmother's heritage, he was – and the record would eventually prove this – spot on."

"But why did your cousin Helen say that?" I asked her, confused.

"Ask yourself that question when you get to be ninety years old, will you?" Aunt Joni replied. "To your point, Helen's mother was Billie's sister. Helen is my dad's first cousin. She didn't remember it because Susan wasn't from her side of the family."

"Oh, okay. Okay. I get it."

"The old-timey picture in the library of my dad and my uncle Paul as young boys – you remember the one I showed you that was taken in the mid-1920s?" she asked. "Helen is the young girl in the photo with them. The two adult women hugging the children in the photo were Anna Pauline – 'Billie' Potter Whitmore – and her sister, Alice French Potter Ligon, their mothers. Helen's mother, Alice, was named after a well-known author who spent time in the area and wrote quite a bit about her experiences in Arkansas."

"So that would be your grandmother and your great-aunt, right?"

"I think you've got it! Helen's family played a role in this part of our history. It was an important role in more ways than one. Helen was a vital witness, given she was the only survivor from those times long ago. She spent quite a bit of time with me over the years, sharing what she could remember. More on her later."

Joni took a sip of her beverage and sat quietly, collecting her thoughts.

"There was another even simpler puzzle related to my dad and his memory of his relations that took me even longer to figure out," she said and paused again.

"What was that?" I asked curiously.

"On several occasions, as I was growing up, your grandfather William referred affectionately to his grandpa Joseph. He once showed me a black and white picture of him as an adult man with fair hair and well-defined features."

"But wait a minute. Now I'm confused. I thought Junius Brown Whitmore was his grandfather."

"And that's right! However, also remember that Richard Augustus and Cornelia's youngest surviving son was named Joseph. Joseph Chrisman Whitmore would have been about twenty-two, maybe twenty-three years old, when his older brother Junius died. William and Paul weren't even born yet. They never knew their grandfather Junius. By the time they were born, Richard Augustus had long passed on as well."

"Okay, but what about Joseph?"

"Joseph would have been in his mid-fifties when my father and his brother Paul were young lads. He evidently became the grandfather figure for them from Murphy's dad's side of the family. It appears Joseph stayed in contact over the years and continued a relationship with his sister-in-law Susan, as his father Richard

Augustus had done. That's why William and Paul would have had memories of him as they were growing up in Little Rock."

"That explains why they called him grandpa! Why did it take so long to figure that out?" I asked her.

"I'm slow," she said, laughing. "If you had any idea how many errors were introduced over the span of our family history that I waded through to get to the bottom of some of this." She paused to drink before continuing.

"I'm getting better at catching myself. Errors can really add up fast. It's true!" I agreed.

"The point being that conscious-based memory seems somewhat of an unreliable ally over the course of time. It's also part of why learning from one another throughout much of human history has been so difficult. There is only so much any one individual might retain. Verbal traditions last if their storytellers survive the chaos of violent overthrows; paper records are easily destroyed – and along with them, the knowledge amassed by the cultures that relied upon such records to carry them forward into the future. Even family photos with names written on the back, I've learned the hard way, aren't protected."

"What?" I asked her.

"Ink and pencil will eventually disappear, given enough time!"

"Oh, wow. I had no idea! That would make a difference."

"Back to the errors contained within one of my family trees prepared by my parents in their later years at the request of my son's father's parents, which incorrectly reflects Joseph as my great-grandfather! By that point in my father's life, even though William had been given his grandfather Junius's name as part of his own, Joseph was the grandfather William actually knew and remembered in his own waning days."

"That's fascinating. It's as if his longer-term memory reconfigured itself to whatever or whomever he could actually remember."

"In this case, as a youngster, William had many positive and loving memories of experiences with Joseph. Nearer to the end of his life, those were what William remembered. Again, Junius had long passed on."

"That's right. This rings a bell from one of my early questions to you about why some ancestors influence us more than others," I pondered out loud.

"Later, when I began to look at this from the historical perspective and saw the intersection of dates and events in Richard Augustus's family and their respective lives, it became obvious what had transpired. And then I remembered Dad telling me as a child that Joseph wasn't really his grandfather. When I asked him how he'd come to bear such an uncommon middle name as Junius, he was clear that it had been his grandfather's. At some point, however, his memory of the facts, versus the powerful memories of his former life and reality, began to break down."

"It's like you're reweaving our family story."

"This one may have been saved in the nick of time, my dear, a family story that was truly coming apart at the seams – for lack of a team of tailors that could gather up its parts and begin to sew the frayed edges back together again after time and distance were done with it."

"Maybe it had to wait until it was ready."

"What was ready?" she asked, tiring.

"The family story, Aunt Joni, *Torch Time Tales*!"

"That's right," she answered, back on track. "It couldn't happen before because the family drama was still unfolding across the generations through my father, me, your parents, and now on to you. I am grateful to the universe for the opportunity to sew such a lifeline for our families moving forward through time. Hopefully, it will prove purposeful enough to stand the test of tradition!"

"I think so," I said excitedly as I got up off the bench. "I think so!"

William Junius Whitmore as an infant in Little Rock, Arkansas, circa 1919–1920.

Anna Pauline "Billie" Potter Whitmore and infant WJW, circa 1919–1920.

CHAPTER 10

Assistance from the Sea

A s with all my visits, each day seemed to be passing
faster than the one before, I thought as I made my way
back from the market along the worn path. My aunt
Joni hadn't felt up to it that morning, and I'd offered
to make the trip without hesitation. By that point, I was plenty
comfortable navigating my way around her neighborhood.

Every day brought new ground to cover. I'd learned a lot in the
process of these visits, and yet I knew there was more – a lot more.
The more I understood, the more I realized there was to learn. My
aunt had a way of helping me bridge miles – and years – in minutes.
If I could only figure out a way to slow it all down, to make it last,
I thought as I arrived back at the house.

As I opened the door, it struck me how far away from home I
was. This time felt different. My home was far away – lifetimes ago,
given this journey. How was I going to remember it all? I didn't
want to forget a thing.

JONI L. WHITMORE
159

To my surprise, upon arriving back, I found Joni in the kitchen. "Hey, you're up!" I exclaimed as I set the groceries on the counter. "I thought you weren't feeling well. What smells so good?" I said all in the same breath.

"Did you get a yellow onion?" she inquired, ignoring the observations I'd made about her health.

Without a word, I found the onion in the sack and passed it to her. I'd learned not to press her on certain subjects I didn't get an answer to the first time. Before long, the smells of simmering garlic and onions were wafting through the house. The table had already been set. I washed my hands and sat down. Joni served up steaming bowls of mussels, clams, and shrimp, set them on the table, and then sat down to join me.

"Welcome home!" she said, raising her glass.

"Thanks," I returned, raising my glass to hers. "This is an amazing feast! I had no idea!"

"Thank you for going to the market! We were overdue for a feast. I've wanted to do this for a while, but I knew I wasn't up to lugging a heavy bag of crustaceans home. So, I negotiated a trade with one of the neighbors, and they delivered the load while you were out this morning. Your timing getting back was impeccable!"

Over the course of the next couple of hours, the two of us talked and ate our way through the three bowls of seafood. Each shell made a unique clapping sound as it hit the discard bowl, creating a back-and-forth, easy rhythm as we alternated tosses into the bowl.

"This is fantastic! A feast like this would cost a small fortune back home."

"In this day and age, a seafood feast costs a small fortune most anywhere," she replied. "And it's important to remember fortunes are relative no matter their size."

"What do you mean?" I asked, licking a drop of garlic butter from my fingers.

"One person's trash is truly another's treasure! One must be able to appreciate and be thankful for what one has. If that's not possible, it really doesn't matter what or how much you have. Nothing would ever be enough for someone incapable of appreciation. Imagine that the only thing you have left in the whole wide world is one moment." Aunt Joni let her voice trail off, leaving me an opening to respond. When none came, she confirmed the registration of acknowledgment on my face before she continued.

"Some of the young women I knew in college came from such wealth. Not only did they have everything they needed, but they'd also been forbidden from working while they were growing up so as not to be distracted from their studies and were absolutely clueless over the relative value of ten dollars – or two hundred dollars! While my own parents gave me much during my upbringing, I never had an allowance. If I had any money in my pocket, it was because I figured out a way to earn it! My perspective on its value could not have been more different from some of my classmates in college. It was in many ways an extraordinary contrast for me to glean during that period of my life."

"I see what you mean. You couldn't take it for granted."

"As a kid, I was excited to learn my parents had opened a savings account in my name at the downtown savings and loan. I received a copper-colored covered-wagon piggy bank in the process to collect spare change to add to my account. But I quickly realized that the initial five-dollar deposit would not amount to much unless I made additions to it. Bless their hearts, I'm sure that was my parents' point. By the time I was ten or eleven, the account had grown to a whopping ten dollars. I remember being crestfallen and discouraged over the tiny size of the amount. Given my age,

I missed out on realizing that, though small, the amount had been left undisturbed long enough to have doubled in value over time. The true importance of that subtlety would have to wait decades to catch up with me, I'm sad to say."

"I never thought about it that way. I've been much more focused on the power of spending over the power of saving. It's clear that's just more of my bass-ackward thinking, isn't it?" We both laughed at that.

"Wealth in any form is valueless if one does not appreciate it, or more importantly, life itself, for the gift it is to us. We are highly socialized and trained to want the monetary reward. It's easy to take life and wealth for granted when they're in front of you every day – when they're all you know. It's a much greater feat to relish every moment and every nickel as your last. Seafood helps," she added, swiping a clam with the last of the garlic butter.

After the cleanup, we moved back outside onto the veranda. It was starting to warm up for the day. I noticed the hummingbirds were already at their acrobatic routines, chasing one another around the yard and then diving into the banana palms for cover in a never-ending game of hide and seek. These miniature motion machines were one of the many reasons I had come to love the place. They really made me laugh with delight. I managed to catch sight of a multi-colored one with a hot-pink neck. And then, before I could even comment on the "hummies," as Joni called them, one of the blue jays landed on the chair next to the couch where she was sitting.

"Okay, here you go," Joni offered. "Watch what happens next."

It was as if she knew in advance what the blue jay was going to do. The jay was looking at me and then looking at my aunt, cocking its head one way and then another. As if on cue, the jay hopped across the top of the back of the chair and then from there to the top of the couch cushion right beside her.

"Was this some of their behavior that you were trying to clue me in about during my first visit?" I asked her, but before she could respond, the jay, having given us both the hairy eyeball, calmly hopped all the way behind her to the other end of the couch and sat an inch off her shoulder. My aunt hadn't moved.

I'd never in my life seen blue jays – who always seemed so skittish – be so comfortable with a human being. On numerous occasions, I had watched them follow Joni as she puttered around the yard, landing beside her like they were old friends just hanging out together.

"What did I tell you? You'd have to see it to believe it!" she said, laughing.

"Do they get this close to you on a regular basis?" I asked, still shocked by the sight.

"It's taken time for them to get this comfortable with me. I have seen an evolution in their behavior with me as the years passed. Initially, they were hesitant about bathing with me anywhere nearby. As the months passed, I would continue to putter away, seemingly ignoring them, and they stopped hesitating when they were ready. Multiple generations of this same jay family now line up one after another for their turn to bathe. It's far more important to the birds than I had realized, especially in hotter climates like California. Before our mulberry tree out front was sculpted and shaped, I looked out the front window early one morning to see more than a dozen birds lined up on the one branch best positioned to get the front lawn sprinklers to spray them. It was clear they needed showers."

Unbelievable, I thought to myself, and yet there it was, another expansion of my perspective on reality delivered literally in my face. There was something else I was missing, though, something very different about all of it, the whole place, not to mention my unusual aunt, but I still couldn't get my head completely around it.

Yet I could feel my spirits getting lighter by the day. Given the state I'd been in when I'd originally showed up, it was a noticeable improvement. That particular awareness was followed by my body signaling hunger.

After our brunch had settled, we spent a couple of hours in the yard, knocking out a few of the items on the to-do list. I sat down to take a break and must have nodded off to sleep for a while. I was startled awake by a pair of sparring gulls crying out to one another as they spun and dove over the pond.

"I believe that's our cue," Aunt Joni said softly. Slowly she began to sit upright, but it seemed to take longer than usual. Her body wasn't cooperating.

Joni acknowledged to me that she was struggling with sharing the next part of the family history. It had taken her father his entire lifetime to talk about it, she mused, so she supposed it was understandable. And yet here she was, with the same difficulty, two generations removed from the event.

"What the heck happened?" I couldn't begin to guess after everything I'd already learned.

My aunt seamlessly shifted gears and talked about the years she'd worked at a women's shelter. She had been in her late twenties before she understood the cycle of violence and the abuse continuum – that is, in a manner that was finally comprehensible to her – and it explained so much about what had gone on in her own lifespan. It was all crazy-making – that much, she knew and shared.

We both understood there was no avoiding what had to come next. We made our way to the house for refreshments and then regrouped on the bench outside. The sun was beginning to set. I'd sensed all day that something was different with her. It was as if I could feel it somehow in the air.

"So, why haven't you wanted to tell me the next part of the *Tales?*" I couldn't keep myself from asking.

"It touches long-buried nerves from my own history, and I've been summoning the courage to go there. This is not easy for me. But I think that if I ease myself back into it, it will help us forward," she offered.

She'd given me enough clues, but I was struggling to put the pieces together. I have to say I was surprised to learn about the cycle of violence and the abuse continuum from my aunt. It explained even more for me about what had been going on in the lives of many people I knew who'd gotten stuck in that damn cycle, seemingly unable to break free.

The sound of Joni's voice brought my attention back to the moment.

"We left off with Murphy and Billie married with two children underfoot – your grandfather William and his young brother, Paul. Six of them were living together in the two-story house on 4th Street in Little Rock. Murphy's nearly grown brother Carlyle, who preferred to be called Ed, still lived there with them, returning to eat and sleep as he pleased. He was his mother's adult baby boy, not yet ready to fly too far from the nest. So, needless to say, it was chaos at best when they were all there together."

"It sounds like a full house, for sure," I commented, trying to be helpful.

"It must have gotten to be too much for them all. I know at some point, at least for a while, Billie and Murphy moved into an apartment on Center Street. That is some of the very recently learned information, by the way."

"I was just going to ask you how you could have known about that."

"It's because, on January 9, 1922, again thanks to GenealogyBank, the *Arkansas Gazette*, and your brother, we know Murphy was arrested by two detectives there on charges of transporting whiskey. They found two gallons of moonshine at the apartment."

"So, he was still doing a sideline in the booze business at this point. Fascinating!"

"He was released on a one-hundred-dollar bail bond prior to the court date the next day. And he would have served time after sentencing."

"It sounds like his sideline business was costing him in more ways than one. It didn't cost him his job at the firehall, did it?"

"No, it didn't. Thanks to the same sources, we also recently learned he was called to account again the following year, in the fall of 1923. Murphy was sentenced to four more months in jail for violation of the Prohibition Act."

"Murphy is sounding like a repeat offender," I said, shaking my head.

"Periodically, Murphy would be assigned to the night shift at the firehall for a spell at a time. Eventually, he began to see the benefit of having a legitimate excuse to sleep all day – or most of it, anyway. At first, Billie wasn't opposed to the idea, although she didn't have a choice in the matter. From her perspective, Murphy would be home in the morning to do a tag team with her before she and the boys left for school each day."

"That doesn't sound so bad," I casually remarked.

"The reality was that Murphy would work the schedule set by the fire chief, which was posted weekly for the crew. If a man refused a shift, which he had a right to within a day, the rotation fell to the next in line – and there was always a line of those needing the hours."

Joni stopped for a moment. I hadn't moved an inch. I didn't want to do anything to interrupt her train of thought.

"As the years went by, and the daily grind of long hours of work with too few hours of sleep began to take their toll, Murphy worked the night shift a lot more – whenever he could get the chance. It wasn't long before Billie noticed the rank odor of alcohol on his breath as he walked in the door in the morning. It was offensive to her, and she told him so. Not long after that, he stopped coming home from work in the morning. She'd get home in the afternoon to find him crashed out asleep – dog tired from long hours working and then drinking with his buddies. His dirty work clothes were strewn from one side of the apartment to the other. Breakfast dishes were piled unwashed in the sink. When he was awake enough to hear it, they argued about most everything. Murphy would only take so much guff from her and then grab his work gear and split for the firehall. It became their nearly nightly routine."

"Yikes. I can see how that pattern would get really old really quick." I offered, shaking my head and grimacing.

"One evening, as Murphy arrived at the firehall, still licking fresh wounds from the tongue-lashing Billie had given him earlier that evening, he noticed one of his crew members bidding goodnight to a smart-looking woman in front of the station. Billie's harsh words quickly vanished from his mind as he found himself immediately mesmerized by the woman on the bench."

"What happened?" I interjected as she paused to take a drink. Aunt Joni didn't respond to me directly. Instead, she chose to continue to make the tale come to life. It was as if I were there!

***

"Hey, George," Murphy called out to his co-worker and then sprinted to catch up with him as he entered the firehall. "Who was that babe? I thought you had a girlfriend."

"Yeah? I thought you had a wife and two children, you dog. As a matter of fact, I do have a girlfriend, and I'd like to keep it that way," the man replied. "So, before you go spreading a bunch of wild-haired rumors, let me set the record straight. That beautiful gal you were leering after is my sister, Vera, you jackass!" The man slapped Murphy on the back. "Now that I think about it, with your history, T.T., you and Vera would have been a match made in heaven – or maybe hell would have been a better fit for the likes of y'all. I'm amazed you two didn't bump into each other in the night somewhere along the way before now."

"Sorry, man, I didn't know you had a sister. And I can't help but notice that you do seem to do well by the ladies," Murphy added, trying to smooth over the man's ruffled feathers.

"Wait till I get a chance to tell her about this," George went on. "She's liable to bust a gut and then hitch up a horse and head on down here, Murphy. You'd better watch your ass! My sister will have a target on yours before you can holler, 'What the hell?' And I'll tell you what. From everything I've ever heard about my little sister, she can either make a grown man howl or leave him to break down and cry, T.T., break down and cry!"

"Oh, yeah?" Murphy asked somewhat incredulously. "I'm quaking in my cowboy boots."

"You will be," warned the man. "You will be, and you can mark my words!" George said indignantly, as they parted to their lockers to change into their work clothes.

* * *

"Little did Murphy know," Aunt Joni said, but then her voice trailed off.

"What? What happened?" I pressed.

"The man was trying to warn him, but Murphy didn't want to hear his words. He fell for the bait, hook, line, and sinker."

My eyebrows raised in high expectation, but not a word emerged from my lips.

"Within a short time, George relayed the story to his sister, Vera, when he saw her next, and true to his words, without further encouragement from him, she made a point to see what all of the fuss was about. A quick check of the weekly firehall calendar told her what she needed to know about when she might cross paths with this mystery man, Murphy. While Vera didn't know Murphy from Adam, she knew she loved a good-looking man in a uniform. And the firehall was chock full of them! She couldn't help it if she had admirers, even if they were married with children."

* * *

So what if he's attracted to me? Vera rationalized excitedly. I'm not going to do anything about it, she argued with herself as she primped. "I'm only going to see what kind of moth I've attracted to my flame," she said out loud, smiling teasingly into the mirror.

One evening, later that week, Murphy was heading to the firehall to report for work when he couldn't help but notice Vera sitting on the park bench out front.

"I understand you were inquiring after me – Murphy, isn't it?" Vera asked disarmingly.

Murphy was quite taken aback by her forthrightness. This was new territory. He'd never been attracted to anyone other than Billie, and she hadn't exactly been attractive to him of late.

Surely, it wouldn't do any harm to have a conversation, Murphy thought as he sat down beside Vera on the bench.

He wanted to know more about this woman who thought enough to call after him at the station. Billie's harsh words from that evening were easily replaced by the soothing coos coming from Vera's luscious lips, and Murphy quickly fell captive to her winning words.

This was a woman who could understand and appreciate him, he thought as Vera stroked his ego sentence by enticing sentence.

* * *

"Geez, Aunt Joni," I interrupted her, unable to hold back any longer. "You could have been a romance novelist!"

"Well, maybe I am getting carried away, but again, I'm trying to do an adequate job of setting the stage for what's coming," she explained. "There's no way around it – otherwise, you just might not believe it was true!" She sighed.

"I'm sorry I interrupted. Please go on."

"From that moment on the bench with Vera, Murphy didn't stand a chance," she replied. "Why should he put up with the treatment he took from Billie when there was a more attractive woman willfully desiring his attention with no questions asked?"

"Ooh, no, he didn't, did he?" I asked in a low moan. "How could he?" After a pause to think about what I'd just said, I added, "Wait a minute – he did the exact same thing his father did, didn't he?"

"Yes, he did," she acknowledged after a pause. "But as you'll learn, Murphy took more steps down that slippery path than his father, Junius Brown, had. And you are correct – Murphy and Vera would soon find their way into bed with one another. It was only a matter of time from that pivotal point together on the park bench."

"Unbelievable!"

"Your great-grandfather Murphy had met his match, and it was all downhill from there." She put her glass on the table and looked at me. "Life-changing events can happen in an instant. One bad decision can ruin a person's life in a moment, I'm afraid to say, but it's true. Many bad decisions piled on top of the first have the potential to ruin many lifetimes."

"Wow," was all I could find to say to her. It was true. I'd seen it myself more than once.

"While it is possible to change course and right some of one's wrongs in life, these incidents, spurred by personal history and heritage, can also combine to have a cumulative impact on the wrong-doer. Imagine a single drop of water, which eventually becomes a stream that finds its way to a cascading waterfall, the force of which builds as it drops lower and lower to the ground, eventually obliterating everything below."

"Geez, that's a powerful image!" I couldn't help exclaiming.

"It was meant to be! We should not underestimate our individual or collective ability to make bad decisions at any given moment. Once made, they tend to concentrate negatively over time. Unless they're identified, they will eventually compound to their logical end. When an unsustainable weight has been created, it drags down everything in its path."

Joni let out a slow sigh and paused. "With every moment, we have the option to build our life or dig a ditch for ourselves. It's your choice – just don't forget the rest of us while you're at it!"

CHAPTER 11

Tail Events

One by one, the stars appeared overhead as the last reflections of sunlight disappeared. It was time to light the torch.

"How much do you know about the Great Depression?" Joni asked.

"Some," I offered sheepishly. "I studied it in school – those were really hard times, weren't they?"

"Your grandfather William and his brother, Paul, grew up in really hard times, yes. Untold numbers lost their homes. Unemployment, poverty, and malnutrition affected broad swaths of the country – like diseases left unchecked to fester. It took years for the country to work toward any form of economic recovery. My cousin Helen remembered looking out the window of her house as a child to the sight of droves of men with nothing better to do, walking the streets of Little Rock during the Great Depression."

"Wow! That would be a sight for a young person to see and attempt to understand."

"Yep. It makes me think of the homeless men in Salem, Oregon, I couldn't help but notice as a kid, lined up around the block and down the street as far as I could see, all waiting for the soup kitchen to open."

"What a sight to have to take in as a child!"

"Survival became the order of those Depression-era years. Things can change quickly when people are living on the edge of life and death. In the spring of 1929, Calvin Coolidge was sworn in as the thirtieth president of the United States. Wall Street crashed on September 3, just a few short weeks before my father William's tenth birthday. His grandmother Susan had reached sixty years old and then died later that year of chronic nephritis, the day before the winter solstice. William's world was forever altered. I can only imagine what all of these events must have looked like through his eyes as a child."

"What's nephritis?"

"She had chronic kidney disease. We'll talk more about that in volume three."

"Okay, and I have to say this is giving me a very different picture of my grandpa Bill," I offered. "It explains a lot!"

"It sure does. I do know my father survived those traumatic times, and I know the scars he bore affected his every waking day, along with his words and actions, for the remainder of his life. He held many of the secrets from those years close, and I suspect he would have taken them all to the grave if he hadn't been induced to reveal them."

"Wow. It's incredible to me that he managed to bury the truth throughout his lifetime!"

"To this day, I'm not clear whether my mother knew what really happened to the man she'd married. My father had long held a 'let sleeping dogs lie' outlook on life. Plain and simple, he didn't see the point of dredging up pain from the past and avoided it whenever possible. It didn't always work out so well for him, I'm afraid."

"What could have been so terrible?" I finally asked.

"It bothered me as a child to hear my grandpa John and other adults say they had lost portions of their memories – especially memories of their childhoods. I vowed to myself to remember as much as I could from that point on. And I became determined to persuade my parents to share their memories with me – memories that might otherwise be lost with time."

"I know what you mean. I've been listening to my dad's short-term memory go for some time now."

"As I was trying to learn about my father's memories of his childhood, I asked him about his mother. And eventually, I wanted to know how she died," Joni explained. "I remember he seemed embarrassed when I asked him the question, which I didn't understand. He hesitated and then explained that his mother, Anna Pauline Potter Whitmore, had died of pellagra during the Great Depression."

"What's pellagra?"

"I asked my father the same question. I remember him struggling with how to explain it to me. After a pause, he offered that the disease was caused by a vitamin deficiency resulting from malnutrition and reminded me that it was during the Great Depression. I had heard of scurvy by that point, and I remember asking him if pellagra was kind of like scurvy, to which he nodded. From my youngest years, I always got the same simple answer from him when I revisited this question. My grandmother had died of something like scurvy as a result of the Great Depression. That's what I grew up believing to be true."

"That's fascinating. And you were able to put it back together from your own childhood memories."

"Yep. I held that belief much of my life. While my father's answer was accurate, it was deliberately incomplete, lacking the extraordinary events in her life that eventually led to her death. When I finally learned everything that had happened to her, I could hardly believe it. All kinds of things in my life began to make more sense."

"Grandpa's decision to keep his cards close to his vest would have been considered a deliberate error of omission, eh? It had to be pretty shocking for all of you when the full story finally came out."

"It was shocking. It's just as shocking – maybe more so – to realize all these years later that it still wasn't even the whole story! However, with time and distance from all of it, I was finally able to begin to put her physical condition into the context and perspective of the times and the science in which she lived."

"Huh? You lost me again, Aunt Joni. What am I missing?"

"My father would scrunch up his entire face and nose as a way to communicate how horrible those times were for folks, and then he would emit a short whistle from his lips as he shook his head at the personal terror of what he remembered. Every time we talked about it, he reacted similarly. The Southern states were hit hard, experiencing the quadruple whammy of the Depression, starvation, alcoholism, and, for many, pellagra as a result."

"I understand the links with the first three, but after that, I'm still missing something."

"Historically, pellagra was referred to as the leprosy of the South. It is a vitamin B3 deficiency, which causes other issues for the body and mind, including dementia. It also appears to be one of the many outcomes directly associated with alcoholism. What I was unaware of is that if left untreated, in those days, pellagra should have taken four or five years to kill somebody. Doctors and scientists struggled for some time to figure it out. The dietary staple of choice for many, corn, which was widely consumed in the South during the Great Depression, turned out to be another one of the culprits."

"Really? How come?"

"Scientists eventually discovered the corn had to be treated with alkali to make the niacin in it available to the body."

"Humph. Amazing! That helps quite a bit, and where did all of that lead you?"

"It led me to the conclusion that the scenes that are about to unfold before you did not play out quickly. In other words, it forced me to look at the probability that both Billie and Murphy had been drinking together for some years prior to the Great Depression. She would have had to have been well on her way in terms of the four-to-five-year time span it takes the disease to kill someone.

"How are you doing, by the way?" Joni asked me. "Have you had enough for the night?"

"You can't be serious!" I exclaimed, exasperated. "You can't stop now."

"Okay, all right. So, the stage has been set for the scene to unfold," she began again after making herself a bit more comfortable. "We left off with Murphy and Vera meeting on the bench outside the firehall. That meeting began a clandestine affair that spanned some amount of time, fueled by long hours without sleep and a lot of alcohol. Vera became all things to Murphy that Billie couldn't give him anymore – especially the attention and respect he'd once gotten from her and then lost."

"I still can't believe he had this affair! It's like he couldn't have cared less about his family."

"Murphy's foul moods made being home a living hell for everybody there – that is, when he bothered to come home. The unending arguments deteriorated Murphy and Billie's relationship to the point where there wasn't anything positive left between them to communicate. William and Paul would have absorbed it all. There was no way for them to escape it."

"I have some sense of what that's like," I threw in, commiserating with William and Paul due to my memories as a child growing up with my parents' sometimes contentious relationship.

"Murphy was sitting at the firehall late one evening when Vera arrived on schedule to keep him company until the shift change, when they would move their party back to her place. Vera found him looking especially ragged and in no mood to be trifled with whatsoever."

★ ★ ★

"How's it goin', sweetheart?" Vera asked, sliding onto the stool beside him. "Anything I can do to help?"

"Yeah," Murphy blurted out belligerently, "you can help me figure out how to get rid of my goddamned wife! She's driving me insane!"

"Listen here, honey," Vera said softly. "Lord knows I have these days myself, but really, this isn't the place to talk about it. Can we save it for later, sweetheart?"

★ ★ ★

"You crack me up, Aunt Joni. Seriously?"

My aunt explained, "As much as Vera might have wanted Billie out of her way, there were too many people around the firehall who might have heard that tirade. Yet Murphy had opened the door, and Vera wasn't going to miss the thoroughfare he'd provided. Between the two of them, they knew just how to get the job done."

"That's creepy!"

"Vera did find a way to bring the subject back around to what had set him off the night before. It didn't take much to inflame the red-hot poker Murphy felt jabbing at him when the subject of Billie was reintroduced. When he stopped ranting long enough to listen, Vera told him that if he was serious, she knew just the person for the job. It would give them cover and distance from the deed itself so they wouldn't be implicated."

★ ★ ★

"We could tell him to make it look like a robbery," Vera suggested to Murphy.

★ ★ ★

"He stewed on it for a while," my aunt Joni relayed to me. "It's only if I factor in the amount of alcohol that he'd consumed by that point in his life that I can imagine him arriving at such a decision. But get there, he did."

"Wow. This is a lot to digest." I said, standing up to give my rising anxiety someplace to go.

"Professionals in the field of domestic violence maintain that alcohol in and of itself does not cause violence," my aunt explained. "They will also acknowledge that alcohol may exacerbate an already violent disposition or situation. Not long after that, Murphy hired a hitman to kill Billie, his lawful wife and the mother of his two children."

"Unbelievable!" I practically shouted, spinning around at about the same time to face Joni, still sitting on the bench. "No wonder you had such a hard time telling me. What an awful way to die, at the hands of a hired hitman – hired by your own husband!"

"Ironically, that's not how she died," she interjected.

"It's not?" I asked, surprised.

"No, it's not. But I'm getting ahead of myself again. I've found it unavoidable at times in telling these *Tales*, I'm afraid to say."

"I interrupted you again. Please, go on!" I fell back beside her on the bench.

"It would have started as a typical school day for Billie and the boys. William was in junior high, and Paul was in grade school. Billie made breakfast, packed lunches, and then herded them outside, locking the door behind her as they headed out that morning. There was no sign of Murphy."

"Humph," I remarked. I had no idea where all of this was going.

"They arrived home not long after one another that afternoon. Murphy was still missing in action. As Billie began preparing supper and the boys did their homework, there was a knock at the door. Without Murphy around, things had been quiet. Billie wiped her hands on a dishtowel and headed to the door. It's not clear whether she knew the man, but evidently, she invited him inside. It's possible he posed as having some kind of delivery or message for her."

"So, what happened?" I couldn't help but ask.

"Before William or Paul knew what was happening, commotion ensued. Billie and the man began struggling. Pots and pans flew about as she attempted to fight off her attacker, but the man had a knife, and he came after her with obvious intent to do harm. It all happened so fast. But then, as if in slow motion, they watched the man raise his knife-wielding fist above his head and then reverse course, driving it down toward their mother's heart."

"Oh, God," I couldn't keep from exclaiming, horrified. "But wait a minute. You said that wasn't how she died!" I blurted out in exasperation.

"I spoke with my cousin Helen about it yet again not long after she turned ninety. I'd turned fifty years old myself a couple of months before then. I called her from the back patio one afternoon to check in. She was my only surviving source on the subject after dad died, and she was more than happy to fill me in on what she could remember."

"What did she tell you?" I wondered aloud.

"Clearly, from the Little Rock side, this was the stuff of family legend, and Helen was delighted to help. William was her favorite cousin, she'd often told me over the years. She loved him like a brother. She called him W.J. Honey," Joni drawled in her best Southern twang. "And he answered to it happily!"

"There's your nearly natural Southern drawl again, Joni," I responded, teasing her a bit.

"Helen reminded me she was a couple of years younger than my daddy, as she'd say, closer to Paul's age. William was her sister Honor's age. She described her mother, Alice, as well as her aunt Billie and all the sisters of that family as tall women, large women. And remember, Billie was a physical education teacher – she had to be in pretty good shape as a result of her job, and she kept her wits about her in the situation she was facing."

"Wow. I just can't imagine! How horrifying!"

"Seeing the blade descending upon her, she turned in the nick of time to protect her heart. The knife blade missed its target and plunged deep into her left arm. Billie took the blow and delivered her own to the killer's shins and privates. With more on his hands than he'd bargained for, the attacker fled out the door. My grandma was alive but wounded in more ways than one."

"What do you mean?" I asked as my hand came up to cover my gaping mouth.

"She'd been stabbed – but more to the point, it jars you to the bone to have someone attack you in your own home. While the man had initially made motions to steal something, Billie knew better. Anyone who knew them knew they didn't have anything worth taking. The man had been sent to do her harm – that much was evident. As far as she knew, there was only one man in the world who might want her dead, and that man was her husband, Murphy."

"It's unbelievable," I said, reclaiming my seat on the bench. "So, what happened?"

"In the moments immediately following, she pressed William into service to help her get a towel tied around her arm. She would have needed pressure on the wound – some sort of bandaging immediately to stem the flow of blood. Paul was sent for help."

"How terrifying for William and Paul to witness such a thing!" I couldn't help but interject.

"I understand now why William eventually blocked out the event entirely, as if it never happened. To experience violence like that in the sanctity of his home would ultimately gravely impact who he would grow up to become. Those moments and the ones that followed between his parents, which were completely out of his control, would end up haunting him the rest of his life."

"Is it typical for victims to forget?" I really had no idea. This was new territory for yours truly.

"Victims of traumatic events do sometimes completely forget them as a way to cope with what might otherwise be incomprehensible and psychically damaging," she explained. "The signs and symptoms of repressed memories will find other destructive ways to emerge eventually, I'm afraid."

"All the stuff left over that they couldn't process, huh? What'd you call that, emotional baggage?"

"That's right. So, Billie survived the stabbing," she continued. "After the attack, it didn't take her long to get back on her feet and find them another place to live. She didn't feel safe in her own home anymore – another attacker might be sent to try and finish the job."

"What a thought to have to live with," I replied, shaking my head.

"It also didn't take long to put two and two together as to what had transpired and who the culprit was, just as she'd assumed. With a little prodding, she eventually got someone to spill the beans. She hadn't known about the affair. No one had wanted to tell her what had been going on between Murphy and Vera for some time."

"Why the hell not?" I couldn't stop myself from interjecting.

"In those kinds of situations, men often stuck together to protect one another, I'm afraid," she added. "Nobody wants to get involved in someone else's business. Wives were admonished by their husbands to keep their mouths shut about what didn't concern them. But put it together, she did – and what she found out eventually helped destroy her."

Joni paused before continuing. I waited to speak, knowing from experience now that it would definitely improve the odds that she'd continue.

"There are several stages to healing from death, loss, and grief, or so they say – and one of those stages is anger. Although cousin Helen had discussed the subject of what had happened on several occasions over the years since news of all of this had first been unearthed by my family and then confirmed by my dad, there was one set of new memories she shared with me over the phone that I hadn't heard before."

"What was that?" I prompted, although I could see she was tiring.

"Well, Billie had finally gotten quite angry with Murphy – one might say she'd gone beyond angry. Perhaps she reacted so differently because this time had been such a close call on her very life and he'd put the entire family at risk with his selfishness and stupidity."

"I'll say."

"Not long after she put two and two together, Billie evidently bought a gun. Cousin Helen recalled how, one afternoon, Aunt Billie showed up at their house in Little Rock, wanting to see her parents. Neither William nor Paul was with her – she was alone. Helen recounted that she watched her aunt pull a gun out of her handbag and show it to her parents." Aunt Joni paused.

"What did they say to her? What happened?" I asked.

"According to Helen, her father told Aunt Billie she knew she was welcome in his house but the gun was not and, when she was done returning it to the safety of the car, she was welcome to rejoin them. Although it had been so clearly imprinted in her young memory at the time, Helen had never shared that memory with me before that point and didn't say more about it, except that it shortly preceded the last stand between Billie and Murphy."

"But I don't understand. Why did she show them the gun?"

"It's hard to say – Helen's parents were close family to Billie, her sister and brother-in-law. They were the kind of family you go to when you've got tough questions to ask. She may have needed help with the weapon. Maybe she was looking for advice – or ammunition. Maybe she was counting on them to get the word out that she was armed. Wisely, her brother-in-law chose not to make a further issue out of it with Helen and the other young children present."

"That must have been eye-popping for Cousin Helen," I remarked.

"It's safe to say Helen never forgot it. Billie might have gotten herself the weapon under the auspices of self-protection after the attempt on her life. It wasn't uncommon in those days for women to have weapons. There were all kinds of predators. It's certainly not clear to me that Billie shared her intentions with them that afternoon – at least, not within earshot of the kids!" She looked to see me wide-eyed again.

"What intentions? What are you talking about?" I asked, still not wanting to believe what I thought she was trying to tell me.

"Hold your horses. I'm getting there!" she replied. "Okay, so, not too long after that visit to the Ligons, all of Billie's anger and anguish about what had happened appeared to converge in a twisted plan for revenge. According to Cousin Helen's account, her aunt Billie took the gun and headed toward the firehall in search of Murphy. She probably didn't expect to find him on the bench in front of the firehall with Vera beside him."

"They were sitting out front?" I was surprised by that.

"Again, according to Helen's recollection, the sight must have been too much for her. Billie parked across the street. She got out of her car and began to cross. Without a word, she raised her gun and started firing. People scattered quickly as the sound of the shots rang out, with Murphy and Vera no exception. She'd managed to miss them, but the damage was done."

"What damage? What happened?"

"This is one of those spots in the *Tales*…" My aunt's voice trailed off.

"Oh, no. What now?"

"This is one of those spots in the *Tales* where the family story and the actual story diverge from one another. What your brother recently found in the press coverage was either long forgotten by William and Helen or, perhaps because of their young age, they were never made aware of the full scope of the incidents."

"What are you trying to tell me?" I asked with a growing sense of apprehension.

"All these years later, we thought the full story had been flushed out, and it was awful enough as it was, but it hadn't been. This whole portion of the *Tales* had been written once already, only to have critical elements and events otherwise completely unknown over all these years come to light in the eleventh hour of this effort. Talk about what would have been a couple of huge errors of omission on our part!"

"Critical events? What the hell else happened?" I cried.

"I have to tell you, it took me a while to figure out this puzzle of clues. Your brother sent me maybe a dozen emails with his latest findings, which arrived all at once one afternoon. My inbox was flooded, and I was elbow deep in the middle of a review and reconciliation of the first copy edit for volume one as it was. So, initially, I was only able to read the very dramatic headlines about this part of it – and after all this time, the new information left me in a state of shock, I'll confess. It was several days later before I could get back in and absorb what had actually happened between the headlines and the articles themselves. I'm afraid I'm going to have to describe them one event at a time, however, and although I'm not Watson or Holmes, I'll tell you right now these two particular and previously unknown events are clearly related to one another."

I hadn't seen this coming, but my growing apprehension was telling me, whatever else had happened, it wasn't going to be pretty. It was starting to ring an awful lot of bells for me around how the Junius portions of the tales just seemed to keep on unfolding.

"Okay, I get it. So, help orient me here. When was all of this again?" I asked.

"The shooting incident took place June 18, 1933," she replied.

"Can we start with the newspaper headlines you read about the event?" I asked, trying to help her through what had to be a confounding set of new developments to digest and then to have to share.

"That's a good suggestion," she responded. "The next day, the newspaper ran three headlines stacked on top of one another. The first headline read 'Mrs. Grace Medley Near Death as Result of Misdirected Bullets.'"

"Oh, my God! Who is Grace Medley?"

My aunt shook her head. "I had the same reaction, believe me! The second and third headlines will help partially answer your question."

"Okay," I said, letting out a big exhale. "What did they say?" I couldn't imagine at this point what was coming next.

"The second headline was in all caps, 'SHOOTER CLAIMS MISTAKE.'"

"Oh, God…! Dare I ask you what the third one was?" I replied with an expression that would have suggested I wasn't sure I really wanted to know.

"The third headline read 'Mrs. Murphy Whitmore Says She Intended to Get Another Woman Seated in Car with Husband.'"

"Talk about a holy cow! Oh, my good Lord! I'm really starting to appreciate what you were trying to tell me."

We looked at one another in disbelief. It was absolutely a good time to take a break.

* * *

"So, what was the relationship between Grace Medley, Murphy, and Vera? Do we know?" I asked when we'd regrouped outside a bit later and the initial shock and aftershocks of all this drama inside of me had quieted down.

"I think I mentioned earlier, when I finally got to read the entire articles, they left me with more questions than answers. However, I can tell you that the original connection between Grace and Vera is pretty clear: they were nearby neighbors to one another. They both lived on Melrose Circle, on the same side of the street, perhaps several houses down from one another, based on the addresses given in the article about this part of it."

"Everything you've shared so far tells me there's more than one part of this tale yet to share."

"That's a true statement. There are several more parts to this tale. The other late-breaking developments will have to wait because we haven't finished the event we're still in the middle of and there's another big part in between them."

"Let me guess – it will throw you off the thread you're on now in the space-time continuum?" I asked her, only half in jest.

My aunt looked at me in mock shock. "Absolutely! You really are a quick study, aren't you?" She chuckled. "How about I pick up with what I learned from the descriptions of the events as they were conveyed by the reporters and the statements by Billie and Vera that were summarized in the article."

"That would be great. Can you do that from memory?"

"At this point, I'm afraid so! It will also allow us to have a better idea of how the events unfolded prior to when Billie arrived on the scene. These are details neither my father nor Cousin Helen could have known had they not read the article or had the contents shared with them by another member of the family."

"Got it."

"In the opening summary, the story said that Vera and Grace had stopped at the firehall to talk to Mr. Whitmore. Although, later in the article, after Vera and Billie were hauled in for questioning, Vera told reporters that she and Mrs. Medley were driving in her car and passed the fire station. She mentioned Grace was driving her car. Vera claimed Grace had seen a fireman she knew, and Vera evidently suggested they pull over and chat with Grace's friend."

"Somebody else was also in this scene?" I asked her, confused.

"No, I think Vera was trying to disguise the fact that it was she who wanted to see Murphy at the firehall, as there was no other mention of Grace's fireman friend, interestingly. Not long after the two women had parked in front of the fire station, Murphy evidently emerged from inside the stationhouse and proceeded to get into the car with them."

"It almost sounds like it was prearranged!" I interjected as the scene played out in my mind's eye. "So, this is the part where Cousin Helen's description of the event begins to diverge, isn't it? They weren't sitting together on a park bench in front of the firehall; they were sitting together in a parked car with another woman in front of the fire station. Have I got this right so far?"

"You are tracking, my dear one. Let's see if I can do the same," she replied, making fun at her own expense. "I know that Billie mentioned in her statement at police headquarters that she had caught sight of the two of them together more than once and had seen him in her arms that night."

"So, how in the hell could she have made such a mistake?" I asked, not understanding.

"I'm reading between the lines just a little bit, but here's what I think must have happened. First off, Billie must have recognized

Vera's car. It's not clear that she'd ever met Vera or Grace before or even seen her close at hand. I think she put two and two together when she watched Murphy climb into a car that she might have seen him get into before. She would have also been able to see there was a woman behind the wheel. She may or may not have noticed there was another woman in between."

"Ah...so, she approaches the vehicle and starts firing at the woman behind the wheel, thinking it's Vera?" I asked.

"Billie did not miss. It appears Grace Medley took three shots at fairly close range. According to the report, Grace was hit twice in the chest and once in her left arm."

"Hold on a minute, can you? Didn't you tell me Billie was stabbed in her left arm?"

"Yes, I believe it was her left arm. You raise an interesting point, that she may have shot Grace there intentionally. There's another possible explanation for this particular gunshot wound that has occurred to me, but you'll need to remind me about this when we get back to Vera's statement to the press."

"Okay. That's interesting. I just couldn't help but see the parallel between the two events and wonder."

"There's a lot to wonder about with all of this, I agree. The reporter said that Murphy got out of the car as the shooting began. At that point, Billie evidently fired twice at Murphy while he was attempting to run away, narrowly grazing one of his ankles, putting a hole through his pants, and nicking his shin."

"Whoa!" I cried.

"As the sound of rapid gunfire filled the air, the firemen would have rapidly spilled out of the station house to see what was going on. Billie wouldn't have been paying attention, as her rage was focused on Murphy and Vera, and I suspect several of the firemen quickly grabbed her from behind. She began shouting at Murphy as he ran away that she wasn't going to miss the next time!"

"Wow! She must have been one hell of a shot to have caught him in motion."

"Here's one of the curious parts. There was a sixth shot fired. But it's not clear to me in what order these bullets were actually fired. If I recall the way the story was written, Vera claimed that after shooting at Murphy, Billie pointed her gun back into the car, aiming straight at her. Vera relayed that she grabbed the gun and turned it away as Billie squeezed the trigger and the shot went off."

"That's really curious." I could see where my aunt Joni was going with this. "So, wouldn't Vera have been reaching past Grace behind the wheel as she attempted to divert Billie's gun?"

"That's my point. There was no explanation as to where the sixth bullet went or even if it was really the sixth shot she'd fired at Billie."

"That leaves quite a bit of room for interpretation of those events. Is that what you were alluding to a few minutes ago?"

"Yes, it was. I was trying to imagine what would have happened when Vera was pushing Billie's gun hand away. We don't know whether Vera or Billie was left- or right-handed. But from Vera's perspective, she could have only pushed Billie's gun hand in so many directions: to the left or the right, more likely. Less likely, she would have been able to knock it upward or downward. She still had Grace in between her and Vera's gun. One direction could have landed that shot into Grace's chest; the other direction could have caused the bullet to hit her arm. Vera did say she'd pushed the gun aside because one of the bullets was intended for her."

"That's a hell of a thought. So, if I'm tracking what I'm hearing between all the accounts, Billie approaches the car, shoots Grace

Medley twice in the chest, thinking she's Vera, and then sees Murphy fleeing toward the firehall and shoots twice at him. By that point, she would have had to have heard or seen that Vera was in the car. Realizing her mistake, she trained her sights to prepare to shoot Vera. Vera appears to have swatted her gun hand aside, and that bullet hit Grace's left arm."

"I think that's a possible scenario, and that's what I was getting at. There are two more curious clues to throw into this mix. The reporter at the scene described Grace as under the wheel. At first blush, I thought perhaps it was an old-fashioned way of saying she was behind the wheel, as we'd say today. But then it occurred to me that there's another possible answer: after two shots to the chest, perhaps she was slumped over or literally under the wheel somehow."

"Wait a minute. You said two more curious clues. What's the second one?"

"We know that three bullets struck Grace and two shots were fired at Murphy, and we're presuming it was the sixth bullet that Vera was able to deflect, yes?"

I nodded but stayed quiet to let her finish her train of thought.

"So, the other curious clue is that Billie turned over her weapon to the police with an empty chamber. She fired the sixth shot, according to Vera. There was no accounting for the sixth bullet."

"That's just really curious, Aunt Joni. So, do you know if Grace, by the grace of God, no pun intended, survived being stuck in the middle of that shootout? What was the headline, that she was near death?"

"Near the very end of the article, it did indicate she'd had surgery and was in critical condition early the following morning prior to the paper going to publication."

"And what about the headline that the shooter had made a mistake?" I asked, trying to understand what had actually happened.

"Evidently, Billie remained at the scene and relinquished her .25-caliber handgun to the first motorcycle cop that arrived. She freely acknowledged that she'd shot Mrs. Grace Medley but that she had intended to shoot Mrs. Vera Hatch."

"Oh, my God! That is just insane! What could she have been thinking?"

"I'm afraid to say Billie's attention was stuck in a state of revenge. She understood that a woman was coming between her and her husband and children, a woman who couldn't care less that she was destroying their marriage and life together as a family. Given Billie's poor state of health, she must have been seriously rattled, both mentally and physically, to have believed that shooting someone was going to make their situation any better."

By this point in the *Tales*, my eyeballs must have been as big as saucers, ready to pop out of my head. Aunt Joni reminded me to breathe. I returned a long sigh. "So, what happened?" I finally asked, too stunned to say much more.

"An ambulance arrived and transported Grace Medley to the hospital. The article relayed that the principals involved were taken to police headquarters for questioning. Curiously, however, while Murphy was named in the article and identified as part of Fire Company 10, there were no statements included from Murphy at all. It's not clear he went to the station. It appears only Billie and Vera were taken to police headquarters for questioning. That's when the reporters had their opportunity to interview them. Billie was described as hysterical and largely unable to speak about the shooting."

"What about Vera? What did she say?"

"Vera acknowledged that it was true she had spent time with Murphy, that they had danced and played golf together, but she claimed they were just friends. She made an effort to separate herself from any insinuation that she'd been intimate with Murphy."

"So, why the subterfuge on Vera's part?" I pondered out loud.

"I suspect she didn't want to be implicated in hiring a hitman to kill Billie. If she was having an affair with Murphy, a married man, she would have had motive enough to face possible legal charges."

"Okay, okay, I get it! Oh! That's just awful!"

"So, the police filed charges of assault to kill against Grandmother Billie and released her after she somehow managed to pony up a three-thousand-dollar bond!"

"How the hell would she have come up with that kind of money?" I wondered aloud. "That's an awful lot to be carrying around even by today's standards."

"Absolutely. I'm assuming there was a local bail bond operation that might have been agreeable to taking some form of collateral against it in the event she was to disappear before the trial."

"Oh, like a piece of jewelry or something?" I offered.

"Yep. Probably jewelry, gold, possibly silver, hard to say. I learned from Cousin Paula more than a decade ago that she'd found an article at the *Gazette* office while she was visiting Helen in Little Rock that relayed Murphy and Billie were both fired from their jobs over the incident – for endangering community safety by their actions."

"They lost their jobs?"

"Yep, and remember, it was the Great Depression. This was a double blow to what was left of that family. There weren't extra jobs to spare and fewer still in the professional capacities the two held. From what I understand, Murphy left town almost immediately – at least for a while. Things were too hot for him to stick around with the potential for the police to start asking him questions about what had triggered the shooting in the first place. He headed west pretty quick. We know from Cousin Paula's sleuthing that his application for Social Security puts him in Hood River, Oregon, not long after that – it listed his occupation as a fruit picker."

"So, what happened with the assault-to-kill charges against Billie?"

"This was one of several parts of her portion of this tale that Cousin Helen had right: she identified Vera Hatch by name correctly; she knew that Murphy and Vera were sitting in front of the firehall together; she identified that Billie had a handgun prior to the event; and she was right about the fact that Billie had missed both Vera and Murphy!"

"And the charges?" I asked.

"And as Cousin Helen sat with that question, I remember her telling me she was pretty sure the charges against Billie had been dismissed. She was right about that as well."

"How is it possible that the charges were dismissed?"

"It is one of the recent items your brother discovered, again, from GenealogyBank and the *Arkansas Gazette*. About two months later, mid-August, I want to say, there was a paragraph that mentioned the grand jury had dismissed the charges against her, with just a brief description of the details of the event itself provided."

"What do you make of that? And is that one of the events you were referring to earlier?"

"No, I didn't include this as a new development because it simply reaffirmed what we already knew from Cousin Helen. As to what I make of the case being dismissed, remember, Murphy had left town. I suspect Vera must have convinced Grace it would be better for them all if they didn't pursue the issue, all things considered. With the two women involved unwilling to testify, especially with one of them having been critically injured, it would have sent a strong message to the police and the city attorneys that there was more to the situation than it first appeared. Billie seems to have been convincing enough – that both her own life and their entire family had been jeopardized. So, with no one willing to pursue the matter, the charges against Billie would have been dismissed."

"Geez," I said and slowly exhaled. "It's just mind-blowing to me how much all of these additional details change the entire scope and scale of the situation from what was originally described to you by Cousins Helen and Paula and confirmed by Grandpa Bill."

"As I've been mentioning, you still don't know the rest of it. And I still can't go there quite yet!" she added quickly before I had a chance to ask.

I shook my head in dismay, disoriented and overwhelmed yet again with the whole damn scene, which just didn't seem to want to end. My lack of response gave Aunt Joni room to begin our wind-down for the night after sharing one more development.

"Over the course of the next couple of years, Billie spent the savings they had left. The odd jobs she could manage to find weren't enough, and she was no longer able to afford the rent. Billie and her boys were eventually evicted from where they'd been living."

"What did they do?" I asked, trying to stifle a yawn. The stars were beginning to really show themselves in the sky. I was always surprised by how many more I could see from her backyard. Without much background light around, the night sky was truly extraordinary there. It was the most revealing view of deep space I'd ever seen.

"You look and sound as tired as I feel. We're going to have to pick this up tomorrow. We've made a day of it," Aunt Joni said, calling it a night.

CHAPTER 12

Blown Away

I remember waking to light streaming through my open window, which had already begun to warm the room. Something wasn't right – it was totally quiet. I usually woke to the sounds of breakfast happening in the kitchen. The silence quickly brought me upright and to my feet. I pulled on clothes and went out into the front room. I could see the door to Joni's room was ajar, and I was relieved to hear her snoring. She'd slept in later than usual. It was the first morning of any of my visits that I'd made it out of bed before she did.

I allowed myself the opportunity to venture back into the library while I waited. The room fascinated me, and I was drawn to all it contained. It was chock full of some of the oldest books I'd ever seen. These were volumes passed down to my aunt from both sides of her family, along with others bought in her lifetime. Some of the books were autographed by those she'd worked with along the way.

One of the works of art in the room was an eight-by-ten-inch embroidery passed down from her mother Eloise's side of the family. It was the work of a nine-year-old girl, who'd embroidered the alphabet, flowers, and trees and added her name, age, and the year, 1823, along the bottom. The framed piece was a powerful visual reminder of my aunt's childhood. It had hung in the breakfast room of her family home in Salem, Oregon, until some point when my grandmother Eloise evidently determined it might be too risky for it to continue to hang. Time and gravity might cause irreversible damage. It was hard to believe I was looking at something that had survived two hundred years in our family.

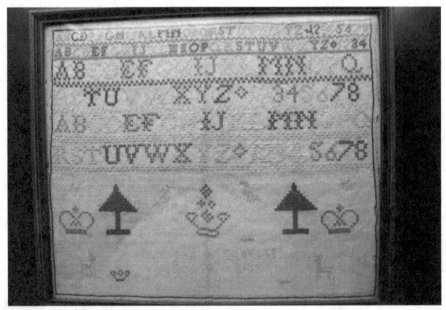

Two-hundred-year-old embroidery that hung in the Whitmore Summer Street House in Salem, Oregon, from the Winn family.

The wall space that wasn't taken up by bookcases was covered with art. I spied an antique, child-size rocking chair that had also been handed down in the family, sitting in the corner of the room. Then

One-hundred-fifty-year-old 'State of Arkansas Bearer bond' from Richard Augustus Whitmore's days in Little Rock.

my eye turned to a large framed piece on the wall – the one my aunt had meant to show me some time ago.

It was an Arkansas bearer bond for five hundred dollars in its entirety – save one coupon clipped for the only interest payment that had been received by the lender. Whoever had possession of the coupons had a right to the interest payments from the state. At the end of the bond's stated term, Joni had explained, the owner or bearer of the bond should have received their principal back from the borrower, the state of Arkansas.

I found myself wondering, with the addition of compound interest, what five hundred dollars would be worth all these years later. If she'd been awake, my aunt might have whipped out her high-tech calculator and figured it out in less than a minute. I'd seen more than once how quickly she could calculate payments for possible real estate transactions.

The Arkansas bearer bond had been purchased by a man with an unfamiliar name – not related. It was likely one of the payments Richard Augustus Whitmore had received for services in lieu of cash. The bond was originally issued in October of 1871. The dates fit. The bearer bond was already 150 years old at that point.

Aunt Joni had distinguished between this particular family story versus the actual story from the get-go. The family story, relayed to her by my grandmother Eloise, was that she'd written the state of Arkansas to pursue the matter and that the state had officially responded in a letter declaring that because it was issued during the Civil War by the Confederate government, they would not honor it.

Following that line of research, decades later, my aunt discovered that the South had actually turned to Europe to raise money for the Confederacy, evidently because Wall Street wasn't convinced of their creditworthiness. After my grandmother Eloise had passed on, my aunt found the actual response to Eloise's inquiry from the Arkansas State Treasurer's office. What was extraordinary about it, Joni explained to me, was that the bond was, in fact, issued after the Confederacy lost power and Arkansas had already been restored to the Union. However, as the state attempted to raise money for reconstruction, con artists stepped in to swindle the bond monies financed for the projects – which were never completed. It happened enough that the voters of Arkansas, by referendum, prevented these bonds from being honored, passing the loss to the unsuspecting bond investors.

As such, the debt that had been issued, including the framed bearer bond on the wall, became worthless. The item apparently had some nominal value from a historical perspective, but for me, it was a preciously preserved window to generations of my family gone by that she'd made come alive.

"There you are!" Joni exclaimed from the doorway. "Good morning! I'm dumbfounded I slept so long this morning; will you forgive me? When I found your bed made and the house so quiet, I thought you might have gone for a walk! How long have you been up?"

"Good morning. Not long. I thought it might be nice for you to sleep in without having to fuss after me, so I've been trying to be quiet," I explained as I got up from the corner chair.

"You have a kind soul," she responded, giving me a squeeze.

We headed for the kitchen to consider what we might have for brunch and agreed that the temperature was just about perfect as usual for a picnic outside in the shade. "I can see why you love it here so much!" I offered as we sat down to eat.

"Help yourself," she replied, handing me a napkin and plate.

I forked thinly sliced meat, cheese, and fruit onto my plate. "So, last night, you left off without telling me what happened to Billie," I reminded her.

"Help me remember where I wrapped up – I told you that both Murphy and Billie were fired for endangering public safety?"

I nodded.

"And that Murphy split town for a while to avoid criminal charges for conspiring to kill Billie?"

Again, I nodded.

"Did I mention Billie and the boys were evicted?"

"That's where you left off," I replied encouragingly.

"Billie was backed into a corner, I'm afraid, and unable to see a way out. Previously, her neighbors and family had been willing and able to help her through her trials and tribulations with Murphy. However, after the shooting, everything changed. People responded differently to her pleas for help."

"Why is that?" I asked.

"Perhaps they stopped perceiving her as a victim of attempted murder and instead began considering her as someone capable of exacting revenge," she replied. "After having made the front page of the papers for nearly killing someone, she must have been the talk of the town!"

"So, what did she do?" I pressed.

"With her savings gone and nowhere to go, Billie eventually turned to her sister and brother-in-law for help, looking for shelter for her family until she could get on her feet again."

"So, they went to live with them?"

"No, no, they didn't," Aunt Joni answered slowly. "I must tell you, Billie was not in great shape – mentally or physically. Studies on the subject suggest that it's when we're tired, highly stressed, and anxious that we are most ethically challenged. But it's not only that. People in crisis often make the worst decisions of their lives. We end up reacting, with little capacity for thoughtful action. Add to those elements that her pellagra was well advanced at that point, which would not have helped."

"What happened?" I asked, perplexed.

"It caused quite a family flap, that's what. It was not a healthy situation for any of them for a long list of reasons," she replied sadly, shaking her head.

"I don't understand."

"After everything that had happened, Billie had nowhere to turn. After their eviction, she showed up with the boys at her sister's house. Cyrus and Alice Ligon sat out on their front porch with Billie for some time that afternoon, talking. It was a difficult discussion. William and Paul had joined their cousin Helen and the neighborhood kids for a game of stickball in the street while the adults talked."

I remember thinking that I might as well have been watching all of this unfold live before my eyes. That's how clearly the scene revealed itself to my mind's eye. It was as if I were there in the street, watching the game and keeping an eye on the adults at the same time. I heard Joni's voice as she continued.

"Ultimately, Helen's father drew a line. Billie and her boys would not be moving in with them. There was simply no room. William looked up from the stickball game in time to see Helen's father going into the house. The screen door slammed loudly behind him. His mother and aunt were still talking on the porch, so William didn't think much about it when he heard Helen's mother call her children by name for supper. The kids gathered up their things and began to shuffle toward the house. As William started to climb the steps to the porch, his mother beckoned him towards her."

"What happened?" I asked in a very quiet voice.

"Billie took William's hands in hers and held them tight. He could tell from the look on her face and the tears in her eyes that she was upset. William could see his mother's lips moving, and from a million miles away, he heard her tell him he was going to have to take care of Paul – and that they were going to be fine. She knew he could do it. William felt his insides begin to turn to water as the meaning of his mother's words sank in."

My aunt looked over to see my bottom lip falling open and the shock registering on my face. She did not pause long before continuing.

* * *

"William felt his mother press some coins and a dollar bill into his palm. You don't have a lot of daylight, son," Billie cautioned him. "I want you to go down to the boarding house near Paul's school and talk with the proprietor about getting room and board. They have a weekly rate. You have enough if you're careful to pay for a week or more maybe – that will hopefully give you enough time to find a job that can support you two."

"Find a job?" William whispered as the full realization of what she was saying sank into his brain. He was all of fifteen. He wouldn't be able to go back to school and work at the same time. He was going to have to drop out of school and somehow support himself and his brother. "But what about you, Mother? What will you do? I don't understand."

"It could take you the rest of your life to understand this," Billie said, squeezing his fingers tightly. "I'm so sorry! The three of us are not able to stay here. It's just not possible. Besides, the money will go farther if it's just the two of you. If you hurry, you might be able to get checked in before they serve dinner."

"But what about you, Mother? What will you do?" William asked again.

Billie was quiet for a moment before she replied, "I'm not sure, honey. I'm just not sure. I guess I need some time to sit with what's happened, to sort it all out. Don't worry about me, you hear me? You're going to have your hands full taking care of your brother."

"But, but…" William stammered, his lower lip quivering as he tried to hold back tears. "Where will you stay? When will we see you again?"

Paul had managed to make his way up onto the front porch by that point, and Billie took her young men into her arms and hugged them close to her. "I'm not well," she said to them. "And I'm not in a position to be able to take care of the two of you. Please don't ask me anymore about it, and do as I've asked you now," she said sternly. "Paul, I want you to mind your brother. Do you understand me?"

Paul nodded, but it wasn't clear to him what he was agreeing to or what had transpired.

"William, you must stay strong, do you hear me? And don't forget – you're too trusting!"

William nodded in reply, too stunned to know what to say.

"Now, get going, you two, on the double!" Billie commanded as she guided them down the front porch steps to the street and sent them on their way.

* * *

Some time passed before I realized Aunt Joni had stopped speaking. I confess I was speechless. This was a blow I hadn't seen coming. In my mind's eye, I was suddenly William, parentless and homeless, transformed in an instant without any forewarning into provider and caregiver, walking down the street with my little brother, with less than two bucks to my name. I felt my body shudder and a bolt of pain course through my butt.

"I don't understand," I finally stammered. "That just sent a bolt of pain through my ass!"

My aunt looked at me with one eyebrow raised. "I know, I know. It is a heartbreaking story. However, what just caught my attention was to hear you make that observation about the bolt of pain in your butt. I learned decades ago that your aunt Lucinda and I both have the same empathetic physiological reaction to witnessing others experience extreme pain. Do you realize that makes our family's bolt-of-lightning-in-the-butt response a genetic one?" she responded, amazed at this latest personal discovery about me in the middle of what was otherwise an extraordinarily traumatic series of events. At that point, all I could do was shake my head and close my mouth.

"It's a lot to swallow, I know," she replied when I didn't respond. "Believe me, I know."

"What about Helen's parents? Why didn't they help – I don't get it!" I was frustrated.

"My own assumptions couldn't have been more wrong," she replied. "I assumed, because of the Great Depression, maybe they were too poor to be able to help. I was well into this before it hit me that something else was going on. What I knew didn't add up."

"What do you mean?" I asked her for the millionth time.

"It's not easy to explain. I went over every conversation I had with Helen. She'd given me clues over the years, but I was too young to appreciate them for what they were. The very first time I met her, on a trip your grandfather and I made to Little Rock, she asked me at one point while we were alone together what I knew about my grandmother. I didn't know much at that point, as I've mentioned, and shared with her that I knew she'd died of pellagra during the Great Depression. I remember Helen nodding her head with an odd look on her face and then changing the subject almost immediately. It seemed strange to me at the time, but reflecting upon it later, it was clear she was on a fishing expedition to see what, if anything, I'd been told. She had enough respect for William to recognize it was not her place to tell me anything more – at least not then."

"Humph," was all I could muster, although I'd been on more than a few fishing trips by that point in my life.

"I'm not sure I could have told you my grandmother's full name at that point, I'm embarrassed to say. It wasn't that I hadn't heard it before, but when Dad spoke of her at all, which wasn't often, he simply referred to her as his mother. When I was a little girl and asked him her name, he called her by her given name, Anna Pauline. I don't remember ever hearing him call her Billie."

"You and Billie are the only two women in our family that I know of that were given male names. That's interesting. It's not that common," I observed.

"You can imagine it wasn't easy to live with," aunt Joni replied. "Anyway, cousin Helen continued to drop hints to me about all of it as the years went by, trying to see if she could get a rise out of me. My travels back and forth in my adult years gave us a number of opportunities to visit her in Arkansas. As I was reflecting on it, it hit me that it was on one of those visits that Helen was especially exasperated with me."

"Why so?" I found myself asking.

"She loved to talk about the family and her relations – those still living as well as those long gone. In that context, she made repeated references to her aunt Billie. I was really trying hard to follow her, but I had no idea who Aunt Billie was, and finally, I had to ask her to explain this particular relationship, which seemed so important to her. Helen stared at me with the most incredulous look on her face and blurted out that Billie was my grandmother in a tone that suggested I had to be an idiot! 'But I thought her name was Anna Pauline,' I replied to her, quite embarrassed."

"'That was her name,' Helen said, 'but nobody called her that. She went by Billie!'"

Your father never shared her nickname with you?" I asked.

"Nope, he never did. I was more than forty years old before I learned what really happened to Billie. When I put her purported fate to my father, William, he confirmed it. And when I asked him why he never told us what had really happened, he initially replied that he wasn't sure, but then he finally acknowledged that he'd been too ashamed and embarrassed to admit it." Aunt Joni let out a very long sigh.

"Wow! That was some serious baggage Grandpa was carrying."

"No kidding," she agreed. "Not long after that, I called cousin Helen and relayed to her what I'd learned. It was as if a dam broke. Helen seemed so relieved that she was finally in the clear to be able to talk to me about it, and out it all came. It's clear Helen needed to talk through what had happened. She was still carrying her own family's baggage as it related to mine, I came to realize, and needed to find some way to reconcile the past as the years progressed."

"I don't get it! Was Helen's family somehow involved in all of this beyond what you've shared?" I asked her, still trying to get the picture.

"I'm afraid so," she responded. "But I think I need to stop for now. It's taken all the energy I have to give today to get this far, and I need to rest."

Needless to say, I was disappointed that Aunt Joni wasn't up for it. She'd left me hanging with more heartache and questions than I knew what to do with, and I stewed on it all late into the night. It hadn't occurred to me how much this was taking out of her until I heard her actually cop to it. I have to say I was too young then to really appreciate how much energy she put into making this so real for me.

Now that I'm nearing the end of my days and trying to repeat with you, my dear audience, what she did for me, I can better relate. So, take it easy on me, okay? Really, I'm doing the best I can. And if I remember correctly, we did take much of the next day off before she seemed ready to continue. I just had to trust that she'd launch in again when she was willing and able. You'll have to trust me to do the same.

CHAPTER 13

Lost in a Century Storm

With her boys gone and the Ligons inside for supper, Billie finally broke down. She was mentally, physically, and emotionally toast. The heated conversation with her sister and brother-in-law had been the last straw. She held herself responsible. No mother worth anything would do what she had just done to her own children, for the love of God.

It seemed the more she'd tried to make sense of it, the more insane it made her. She'd been angry with Murphy, it was true. She'd been angry enough to try to kill him. Surely, anybody could understand that. She suspected others would have reacted similarly after discovering an infidelity and an attempt on their own life – enough to destroy them and their children.

But to have her own family turn their back on her and her boys. How could they? Billie's anger began to refocus on Cyrus. Just one more knife through my heart, she chided herself cynically.

What's another at this point? But for Cyrus to refuse her children shelter was unforgivable, and she despised him for it. As much as her sister Alice had pleaded with her husband that day, he had been unrelenting. It was clear he had his reasons. Billie didn't have to like them.

What a cold-hearted son of a bitch my sister married, she mused. We both got one cut from the same damn bolt. And then it hit her with full force. She had failed in her attempt to exact revenge on Murphy. But there was a way to make Cyrus pay for his decision – and regret it for the rest of his life.

* * *

Inside the Ligon household, things were winding down for the night. The servants finished in the kitchen and bid the family goodnight before heading out the backdoor to their cabin. The children had been put to bed. It had been a dramatic day, to say the least.

"Thank heavens Prohibition is over," Alice said with a sigh as she poured herself a stiff one. She took a cigarette from Cyrus's pack on the counter and headed to the front hallway. Alice opened the screen and stepped outside onto the porch. The last person she expected to find was her sister Billie, who had fallen asleep in the rocking chair.

"Oh! Good God!" Alice cried out, knowing full well Cyrus would blow a fuse when he learned Billie was still there. She couldn't bring herself to wake her sister, much less make her leave. She was flesh and blood. They'd shared everything since she was old enough to remember. Alice had been called worse than cold before, but this was where she drew the line. At the end of the day, she had to be able to look at herself in the mirror. If Cyrus wanted Billie put out on the street, he'd have to do it. She'd have no part of it, she decided then and there.

Alice returned to the kitchen and poured a glass of iced tea. Then she grabbed a comforter from the couch and took them outside. She set the tea beside Billie and gently covered her. The whole situation was tragic. She couldn't believe the position Billie and Cyrus had put her in – to think that she should have to choose between her husband and her sister and children, to choose amongst family. A growing knot was developing in her gut, and she shuddered with the anxiety of not knowing how this horrid drama would play itself out or when it would finally end. Regardless of how it played out, it was clear there was no fairytale ending in their future. It had been an ugly day.

Alice returned inside and went to bed. Cyrus was reading the newspaper, like he did every night before he fell off to sleep. She gave him a long, cold, hard stare, daring him to say something to her, and then began to undress.

"Alice, honey," Cyrus began, seeing his wife was still furious and knowing full well why.

"Don't you honey me!" she replied sternly. "She's still out there on the front porch. And if you so much as think about waking her up or making her leave, I'll be right down the steps after her, and you can kiss my ass goodbye. Do you understand me?"

Without a word, Cyrus folded the newspaper and took off his glasses. He rolled over and pulled the sheet up over his shoulders. Cyrus was a smart man. He knew when he was beaten. His wife had played the only card she had left – and he wasn't about to call her bluff.

CHAPTER 14

Last Light near Darkness

William didn't say much to Paul as they walked down the street in the direction of the boarding house his mother had suggested. He wasn't sure what he was going to do if they were full. He supposed he'd have to cross that bridge when they came to it.

All he knew for sure was that his stomach was in knots and hurt like hell. It wasn't like they'd had a lot to eat that day. His heart was racing and felt like it could pop out of his chest at any moment. He hadn't been this scared out of his wits since the hitman had attacked.

Be strong, be strong, William repeated to himself. Paul was carrying on about the stickball game – one of the cousins hadn't played fair. "Will you be quiet and let me think?" William snapped. "Don't you realize that's the least of our problems?"

Paul drew quiet and tried to keep up.

William was just about beside himself with anxiety. If he didn't find a bathroom soon, he was sure to have an accident. If that happened, nobody would want them. His hands were trembling. Be strong, be strong, he repeated. It was a distance to the boarding house near Paul's school. The two brothers arrived at the door as the last light left the sky.

"Listen to me, Paul," William said before they went inside. "I want you to be quiet and let me do the talking, you hear me?"

Paul hadn't spoken since William's warning, but he threw him a dirty look for good measure anyway.

William opened the door, and they went inside. The small lobby was empty save for a couple of chairs and a registration table. A sign said "ring for service." William hesitated and then brought his hand down on the bell. The clang startled him – nearly more than his nerves could handle. He stuck out his arm and pointed to one of the chairs, and Paul sat down.

Before long, a heavyset woman emerged from down the hall. She found two skinny-neck punks in her entryway and shook her head sadly. The two looked decent for street kids – she'd seen worse-looking urchins running around. "I'm sorry, son. We don't have any more food today for beggars. Have you tried the church down the street?" she asked, assuming they were there for a handout.

William's heart sank again but couldn't seem to find a bottom. He felt his anxiety rising faster than he could manage. They didn't have a plan B. "Excuse me, please, ma'am, but I'm here to inquire about room and board for me and my brother, ma'am," he heard himself stammer.

"Oh? Well, now," the woman replied, "that's a horse of a different color. What's your name, son?" She eyed him.

"My name's William Junius Whitmore, ma'am, and this here's my brother, Paul Gene."

The woman continued to eyeball the two of them as she considered the request. "Well, William Junius Whitmore," she inquired, "if I did have a room for the likes of you, how long would you be aiming to stay with us, now?"

William wasn't prepared for this. His mother's warning that he was too trusting rang louder in his head than the service bell. He didn't want to open the whole can of worms. The less said, the better their chances for the night. "We'd, uh, be interested in, uh, your weekly rate, ma'am," he stammered, suddenly remembering his mother's advice.

"Our weekly rate, eh?" the woman replied, surprised. "And how much are you aiming to pay by the week, son?"

"I don't rightly know, ma'am."

The proprietress was quiet for a moment as she pondered these curious kids. Someone had sent them her way. Business of the paying variety was the best kind of all – and she was loath to turn away paying customers when she could help it. "Well, I'm sorry, son. All of our regular rooms are sold out." She watched as William's facial expression transformed from nervous to downright panicked.

"Please, ma'am," William pleaded in crisis as the last hope for a rug for the night was being pulled out from underneath him. "We wouldn't take up much space if you could spare us a little somewhere. And we're willing to pay something. Please!"

The proprietress eyed him suspiciously. "How much money you got, son?"

There it was, the one question he'd hoped to avoid answering, at point-blank range. And there was only one thing left to do. William reached into his pocket, pulled out the coins and dollar bill his mother had given him, and put it all on the table. "That's all we got, ma'am. I hoped that would buy us a couple of weeks – until I could find me a job."

"Well, I'll be darned," she replied, looking at the pile of money on her table. "You're serious about this, ain't ya, boy?"

"Yes, ma'am," William replied.

"Well, even if we did have one of our regular rooms available, you two wouldn't be able to afford it long," she declared. "But I tell you what. I do have a small attic room upstairs over the street I could let you have for cheap. We don't ordinarily rent it – grown men can get downright mean after they've banged their noggins on the low ceilings one too many times. I suppose, if you'd be agreeable to washing dishes to contribute toward your board, I suspect we might be able to reach an agreement," she concluded matter-of-factly.

William stuck out his hand as fast as he could to strike a deal with the proprietress before she changed her mind. Within seconds, she was pointing him toward the toilet, and not a minute too soon.

CHAPTER 15

Nightmare in the Making

B illie struggled to wake up from a nightmare and realized she was still on the Ligons' front porch. The neighborhood was asleep. She looked down and recognized the comforter from the living room and pulled it over her lap. To her right, she noticed the tea, the telltale lemon sunk to the bottom. She raised the glass and took a sip. It was sweet, the liquid soothing. She hadn't had much to eat or drink for some time. The boys had needed it more.

It wasn't long before she heard the servants make their way up the back steps to begin preparations for the Ligons' morning breakfast. Shortly, the household would be up and getting ready for the day.

Billie began to piece together what happened, but her head was pounding, and her heart ached. It felt like she'd been stabbed again, but this one hadn't missed her heart. Sending her children away was the toughest thing she'd ever had to do. She wondered if they would forgive her, if they could ever understand. Every part of her life that she'd been silly enough to take for granted had been wiped away. It was all gone. Her boys, marriage, job, their home, and all their things – everything she'd worked for – gone. There was nothing left.

Cyrus was the first Ligon out the door that morning. He cast a stern glance in her direction, and Billie's eyes met his full-on. He didn't appear to be surprised to see her still there. Lunch pail in hand, Cyrus descended the steps and headed off to work.

Mary, their oldest daughter, was next out. Helen was not far behind. They seemed surprised to find her there.

"Good morning, girls," Billie offered them.

"Good morning, Aunt Billie," Mary and Helen replied in unison.

Billie watched as the girls clutched their books to their chests and made their way down the street. She felt sick to her stomach all over again about her boys. William was almost through the eighth grade. As a teacher, she was thoroughly ashamed. She knew what dropping out of school might portend for the future of her children in these hard times, and she shuddered. William and Paul were bright young men and deserved better.

"How could I have been so stupid!" she exclaimed, recalling the cascade of decisions she'd made that had brought her to that point on the porch.

"You weren't stupid, sister," Alice said as she emerged from the house with baby Lorene in her arms. "You fell in love," she added, sitting down. "There is no intelligence where love is involved – at least to my knowledge. You of all people ought to know that by now, sister!"

CHAPTER 16

Adrift in a Lifeboat

illiam woke in a panic and opened his eyes to
see the unfinished eaves of the boarding house
roof just above him. Paul was still asleep. It
was already warm in the little room, with light
streaming through the window. He flashed on his mother sending
them away and felt ashamed and alone. The fear and pain in his gut
were back with a vengeance as emotion and anxiety combined to
overwhelm him. He felt like he might suffocate.

William slid the latch on the window and managed to get it
open, but it wouldn't stay. Just that little bit of fresh air to breathe
was a relief. His eyes canvassed the room for something to hold it.
"I guess I won't need these anymore," he said, grabbing one of his
textbooks to use for a prop.

"What do you mean?" Paul said as he sat up in bed, awakened by
the sound. "Why won't you need your books anymore?"

"Because I'm not going back to school," William answered. "But you are, and if you don't get moving, you're going to be late!"

"Why not?" Paul asked, beginning to get up. "Why aren't you going?"

"I'm not going back today or any other day. I've got to find a job to support us."

"What about Mom?"

"What about her?" William said, feeling the lump in his throat. "She can't take care of us now," he added quietly, hoping Paul would drop the subject.

Paul heard his tension. "What about Dad?"

William stopped in his tracks and stared at his little brother in disbelief. "Have you seen Dad anywhere around lately?" he asked sarcastically. Paul didn't respond. "I didn't think so. Now, come on. We've got to get you to school. Thankfully, it's not far."

* * *

That morning, Alice got serious about asking Billie what she was going to do. She was done being polite. Billie had to do something – anything but sit there on the porch and stare into space.

"What are you going to do?" Alice demanded to know.

"I don't know," Billie replied, shaking her head listlessly.

"Are you ready for some breakfast?" Alice asked more gently, satisfied that at least she'd gotten an answer out of her and still not feeling so hot about her role in what had gone down there yesterday.

"No, I'm not," Billie replied firmly.

"Virginia!" Alice shouted at the top of her lungs to one of her servants. "Come help me with Lorene, will you? She's all wet!" Alice felt the bottom of her youngest daughter's drawers.

Virginia came out the front door, whisked the toddler from her mother's arms, and then just as quickly disappeared.

"Well, let me at least get you some more iced tea, okay, honey?" Alice said, rising from the rocker.

There was no response. Billie was resting with her eyes closed.

Alice took the nearly empty glass off the porch rail near Billie and went back into the house. When she came back out with a fresh glass, Billie appeared asleep. Alice left the glass and her sister alone.

★ ★ ★

William and Paul were slowly winding their way down the old, rickety stairs to the main floor of the boarding house. The proprietress had failed to clue them in to the fact that there were six flights of stairs up to their attic room. It had taken all the energy William had left to make it up the stairs the night before, and he recalled falling onto his cot, exhausted.

The smell of biscuits reached their nostrils as they approached the kitchen. "Here, you two. There's one for each of you," the proprietress said as she handed them each a buttered bun with jam, wrapped in paper.

William and Paul accepted their packages, and each managed a polite thank you. They were hungry. William flashed to how much food his mother had given up that week so the two of them would have something. He would never forget it.

"Why, you young gentlemen are most welcome!" she responded, delighted to have manners in her house. "Supper is served at six, so don't be late – remember, there are no leftovers for latecomers!" she warned as they were heading out the front door.

"And don't forget our deal, William Junius Whitmore. After dinner, your time is mine in the kitchen!" she hollered as they crossed the street to the elementary school.

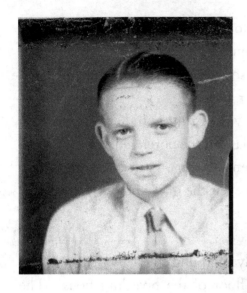

William Junius Whitmore in Little Rock, circa 8th grade.

★ ★ ★

Across town, at the Ligons', Alice went back outside to check on Billie. Her sister had hardly moved an inch, and the glass of tea Alice had brought her that morning still hadn't been touched.

"Hey there, sister," Alice said, nudging Billie's arm. "Wake up now."

Billie opened her eyes and looked at Alice. No words emerged from her chapped lips.

"Are you ready to have lunch, honey? Do you want anything to eat?" Alice asked.

Billie shook her head but didn't speak. Her head fell back against the rocker, and she stared blankly into the street. Alice peered intently at her younger sister, clueless as to what to do to help her. She wasn't looking good.

"Do you want me to call a doctor?" Alice finally asked. Billie shook her head again and closed her eyes. Alice didn't see the point in trying to press her and returned inside.

★ ★ ★

William did get Paul to school that day – just shy of the bell. "I still don't see why you get out of school and I don't," Paul complained as he opened the door.

"I'm older, that's why. I'll meet you here at three, okay?"

William waved as his little brother disappeared inside. Then he walked back to the street. He had no idea where to look for work. Anxiety came on in waves and quickly overwhelmed him. He crossed the street and ran to the boarding house, taking the stairs two at a time. He was in the door and to the bathroom before the proprietress could make it to the parlor to see who'd come in unannounced.

After splashing cold water on his face, he looked in the mirror and saw dark red blotches all over his neck. Oh, great. I look like a wreck! "Nice to make your acquaintance, sir," he said to the mirror, imagining what a potential employer would think of him looking like he'd been to hell and back.

William opened the bathroom door and came out into the foyer. The proprietress was seated in one of the lobby chairs, waiting.

"Come join me," she said, patting the chair beside her. "It's clear something's going on." She paused as William hung his head in shame. "You can talk to me about it if it would help."

That small kindness and the invitation to talk was all he needed to hear. It was all too much for him. The woman placed her hand on his shoulder to console him. Given everything, including his mother's parting warning, he was pretty sure he couldn't trust anyone, and he had no idea how she'd respond.

"That's one hell of a story," the woman finally responded when he'd finished recounting what had happened to them. "And if I hadn't kept up with my newspapers on a regular basis and seen some of them articles about your mother and father, I might have thought you were making it up!"

William looked at her quizzically. He wasn't in the habit of reading the paper. It never occurred to him that everyone in Little Rock knew what had happened. He found his head back in his hands, nearly nauseous. He imagined his hell could get quite a bit deeper.

"When you came in last night and introduced yourself, I knew your name sounded familiar, but I just couldn't place it," she said quietly with a concerned expression. "How can I help you?"

"You already did, ma'am," William responded. "You made a place. That was more than we had last night. I can't thank you enough! I'm just sorry to burden you with our trouble."

"No burden here," she assured him. "Have you thought about what you might do for work?"

"No." William shook his head. "I wasn't expecting to be homeless today, much less hitting the streets for work. Before we were evicted, I had a paper route, and I would have been in school today had all of this…" His voice trailed off as the tears welled up again.

"These are damn hard times, William!" Marge said to him as she handed him a hankie. "You know there are countless men, women, and children out there looking for work – anything to keep their heads above water. There's more arriving here from someplace else literally every single day. Believe you me, I know what I'm talking about when I tell you it's a mean, ornery world out there, and you got to fight like hell to survive!"

William had never heard such a perspective before, but her words hit home for him in ways he had never imagined possible. They were words he would never be able to forget. His heart sank further into his stomach. He dropped his head into his hands and began pulling on his hair.

"Hey, hey there," she said to him. "The good news for you is that you came to the right place!"

William looked up. "I did?" he asked skeptically.

"That's right! I've lived here a long time, and I know lots of people. We'll put our heads together and figure this out. What d'ya say?"

"Okay, I guess," William timidly agreed. "We don't have anything left to lose."

"That's more like it! You see, we all got to get round to hittin' bottom at least once in our lives in our own way and our own time. If we don't learn how to pick ourselves up afterward and go on, we may never learn! That there'd be a darn shame, now, wouldn't it? Lord knows I've had my share of help along the way."

Before William could blink, the proprietress reached into the desk for paper and pen and scribbled out a couple of business names, their addresses, and the names of the bosses that William should try to see.

"Here you go. Do whatever's in your mind to do, but if it were me, I'd go see if you can get yourself hired back with the newspapers. Tell George his guy hasn't shown up for a week here and I don't think he's coming back. If you tell him Marge Goodbody sent you, you might just land yourself a job right out front here!"

"You really think so?" William asked, his eyebrows rising with a hint of hope.

"And when you're done with the paper, you oughta head over to the other place here on the list and put in your application – and be sure to add your work history. It looks better if you have prior experience and a job that you're looking to improve upon than be lost in a pile of desperate unemployed folk who don't know anybody. List me as your reference. That'll tell 'em you got local connections and you ain't just some fly-by-night punk. Got it?"

William sat up straighter. "Thank you, ma'am. I can't thank you enough."

"No problem," she assured him. "But there is one thing you could do for me."

"What's that, ma'am?"

"Call me Marge! There's no point in us bein' so formal with one another 'round here."

"All right, ma'am, I mean Marge," William corrected himself. "Thanks again for your help!"

"Why don't you save your thanks until we can get you a job?" she replied, slapping him on the back like an old-timer.

"Okay, but there's just one problem. I told Paul I'd meet him across the street at three. What if I'm not back?"

"Now, don't you fret. If you're not back here by quarter of, it'll be my cue to walk over to the school and escort him."

"You, you would?" William stammered.

"You think I'm dumb enough to let my new dishwasher slip through my fingers because he can't pay his rent? The way I see it, we're partners now!"

William found himself speechless. He'd lost his home and his parents and was now an eighth-grade dropout, but somehow he'd managed to gain a partner. For a few moments, he regained focus – long enough to get a grip on what needed to be done before the anguish swamped him all over again. He was grateful for her kindness.

Marge, as it turned out, was right on the money. The newspaper boss did hire him back. William could hardly believe his luck. It was a good location, and his quota went quickly. His next stop was the Western Union Company.

"You can borrow my bike," Marge offered. "When you get the job, you're going to need it. I'll make you a deal!" she hollered after him as he sped off.

As predicted, Western Union needed someone who knew their way around Little Rock, was capable and reliable, had references, and could start the next day.

* * *

Helen walked up the front steps behind Mary and nearly bumped into her from behind. Mary had caught sight of Aunt Billie sleeping in the same place they'd seen her that morning.

"Look, Helen – it's Aunt Billie! She's still here. That's strange. I wonder if she and Mother were up late playing cards last night," Mary said suspiciously.

"That would explain it!" Helen agreed.

"Come inside, girls, and let your aunt Billie rest," their mother said from inside the living room. Alice had been fretting all day about how Cyrus might react. She didn't like being caught in the middle one bit. There was always a chance he could blow a fuse.

"How long is she planning to sit out there?" Cyrus finally asked Alice after dinner that night when they were alone. He'd made a point to avoid the ugly topic all evening.

"I'm not sure," Alice replied slowly. "She's beside herself, and I don't blame her. You do realize that after your selfish declaration that there was no room for them here, she sent those boys down the street with not more than two bucks between them. We now share some responsibility for whatever happens to those boys, given your refusal to provide them shelter. They are our family, Cyrus! As to Billie, quite frankly, Cyrus, I'm not sure what to do!" She threw her hands into the air.

* * *

As agreed, when William failed to return, Marge met Paul and escorted him back to the boarding house that afternoon. By the time

William returned from Western Union, it was nearly dinnertime. He went into the washroom and let out a bellowing sigh of stress. Twenty-four hours had passed since they'd been on their own, and he had two jobs. His painfully empty stomach reminded him that dinner was about to be served.

William found Paul seated at the table and took an empty chair beside him. He looked around at the grown men. Some nodded in return; some didn't. Marge wheeled in the serving cart from the adjoining kitchen. The sight and smell of the steaming food were almost too much. They watched as the men served themselves, wasting no time digging into the serving bowls.

"Y'all better not be quite so polite – dig on in!" Marge instructed William and Paul. "These men have one leg up on you. With things so dang bad, we revised the house rules some, and I may have forgotten to mention it to y'all. So as none of you can put us out of business with your insatiable appetites, I serve one less portion of everything I got than men at my table. Don't worry, you'll get something here to eat, but if you don't choose what you want most first – you might not get any! I know I warned you this morning there were no leftovers for latecomers, so get busy!"

William began to get the picture. Ten tough forks swiftly removed ten slabs of ham. There was one slab left, and neither William nor Paul had any. As they watched, portions of everything else disappeared.

"Why don't you two split this one," Marge said as she picked up the ham plate and extended it to William. "Then I can at least get one dish off the table." She saw the look of dismay register on William's face as he lifted the slab onto his plate and cut it in half for Paul.

"Now, what was I telling you this morning, William?" Marge goaded. "It's a mean, ornery world out there, and you got to fight to survive! Didn't your parents teach you anything?" she added without waiting for a response. "Don't fret! You'll get faster. I guarantee it!"

★ ★ ★

By this point, I couldn't help interrupting, which was a shame because Aunt Joni was really on a roll. "Are you making this up? How could you know this?" I asked her, dumbfounded.

"When your grandfather talked about his memories from the Depression, I couldn't help but notice a predictable shift in his demeanor," she explained. "He clearly loved his mother, yet those painful memories made him so uncomfortable. When the focus shifted to how he managed on his own with Paul, he would get a lift in spirits and sense of pride about himself as he talked about their life at the boarding house, that he'd been able to care for himself and Paul on his own. Decades later, he was still astounded by the nerve of Marge's boarding house rules. And yet something in his expression suggested that he admired her for keeping her head together in those brutally tough times. He never failed to shake his head in amazement at her audacity. Ironically, she was modeling for him what it appeared to take to become a survivor."

★ ★ ★

Marge Goodbody was right in more ways than one, William thought to himself. She'd been right about how hard the fight to survive really was. It wasn't easy battling the streets of Little Rock on his bike, making deliveries every day. The faster he rode to his destinations and back, the more jobs he'd be assigned and the more he could make. It was harder than it looked – his first nearly full week had left him spent, and Friday would be even heavier still, he'd been told.

★ ★ ★

"That week at Helen's house with Billie on their front porch wasn't a cakewalk, either, and the situation had taken a turn for the worse," my aunt began the next evening. "Billie was having her own battle at the Ligons', a fight for her life, which she was no longer willing to defend. Each day further turned the screw. It was only a matter of time," Aunt Joni added quietly.

★★★

The Ligon girls had begun to suspect something was wrong. Aunt Billie had been in the same spot on the porch every morning and afternoon for over a week – as if she hadn't moved in between. There was the same telltale glass of iced tea perched beside her, always full. The girls had noted that she hadn't greeted them at all in the last several days – she seemed to need to sleep. Mother kept barking at them to let her be.

With each passing evening, dinnertime became less and less pleasant in the Ligon household, and the atmosphere was more charged than normal. The servants had stopped bothering to ask whether they should set a place for Billie at the table. Nobody spoke, and eye contact was brief.

After bedtime, the girls heard a heated conversation between their parents through the floorboards, but the words were unintelligible. Eventually, things quieted down.

The next morning, as Helen and Mary were leaving out the front door for school, they found the rocker empty. "I wonder where Aunt Billie went," Helen mused, startled to find her gone.

★ ★ ★

William had ridden hard that day, and he was feeling it in his calves. He'd gone back to Western Union to pick up the afternoon deliveries. These next several hours would be the toughest. Rush hour would begin soon. It was the most dangerous time for a delivery rider, and he and the other riders were warned every day to be careful.

Back on his bike, he made it out to the main thoroughfare in no time. It had been a brutal week – his mother was never very far from his mind. He found himself looking for her every time he glimpsed a woman as he rode, and he secretly hoped he might spot her and that all might be right again.

William was riding hard alongside the traffic when he heard and then spotted a newspaper boy not far ahead at the corner, hawking papers. "Evening edition, headline, headline! Read all about it!" As William passed by, his eyes traveled like arrows to the photograph on the front page, and he felt his heart jump hard out of his chest. It was his mother.

A loud screech of brakes and the sound of twisting metal followed. William never saw it coming. He felt a sharp thrust of pain in his leg and went soaring like a bird in flight. It was the last thing he remembered before losing consciousness.

CHAPTER 17

Flotsam and Jetsam

William woke up in the hospital. He opened his eyes to see a long cast extending out in front of him and recognized his toes sticking out the other end.

"You're a lucky young man!" he heard a sweet voice say.

"What happened?" he managed to whisper.

"You were hit by a car!" The nurse informed him. "It's amazing you survived! The doctor says it was a clean break, and he set it right up for you. You're gonna live! It's William, isn't it?"

"How'd you know my name?" he croaked back.

"You were a mystery for a while, but we figured you out!"

"You did?"

"Your Western Union uniform was a giveaway!" She laughed. "We called your office – they determined it was you as soon as we gave them your rider number."

William reached up to feel bandages around his head. Then it all came flooding back as he flashed to his mother's face on the front page.

The nurse consulted his chart. "You need to get some rest now," she said firmly as she began to leave. "Your uncle Cyrus will be here later to pick you up."

William felt his throbbing head and drew quiet. Once again, his future had been tossed in the air like so much confetti. He turned toward the last light of that day and realized there was a man asleep in the bed next to him. Sleep felt like a safe place. He closed his eyes and wondered about Paul. Maybe he'd had the sense to go back to the boarding house after school and stay there like he'd been told.

* * *

It had been a hellacious twenty-four hours at the Ligons'. After a terse debate with Alice the night before, Cyrus concluded that Billie should go to the hospital. It made no sense to have her die on their doorstep. With the help of the servants, she was carried out to the family car and laid across the back seat. Cyrus would have to drive. Alice stayed with the girls and baby Lorene, asleep upstairs.

The emergency room was busy when Cyrus arrived that night in early May. He'd broken a sweat. The hospital staff did what they could, but it was too late for medical help. Billie's death was imminent. Cyrus filled out the paperwork for Alice's sake as next of kin, signed his name, and went home. Alice was sitting in the rocker on the front porch when he arrived. Neither ventured a word to the other.

Cyrus had to be at work early that next morning. He was a Missouri Pacific Railroad conductor, and a bad switch had left his train stranded on the west side of town.

When he finally made it back to the office, he found himself tired from all of it. The week of drama and upset at home flashed before his eyes. Then his strained back weighed in, and he pictured himself lifting Billie's limp body out of the car at the emergency room. He'd missed his lunch and was trying to swallow some aspirin for a pounding headache when the phone rang for the umpteenth time that day.

"Hey, Cyrus! Line two is for you!" a voice shouted from the other room.

"Who is it?" Cyrus yelled. He was in no mood to be messing around on the phone.

"Some lady named Marge Goodbody!"

"Never heard of her! Take a message, for crying out loud – can't you see I'm busy?" he thundered back.

"She says it's important! You'd better take it!"

Swearing under his breath, Cyrus picked up the receiver. Marge Goodbody introduced herself and left him no time to get a word in edgewise. She cut straight to the chase. She understood that they were both busy people. She'd just gotten off the line with Western Union. William had been in an accident. He was at the hospital with a broken leg and would be ready for release shortly.

"What the hell has this got to do with me?" Cyrus yelled into the phone. For the life of him, he couldn't believe his luck with that family. First Billie and now her kids. He'd warned Alice years ago that there'd be trouble when Billie got hitched to that no-good half-breed-turned-two-timing husband of hers. What did she expect, that they would live happily ever after?

Marge explained that William had listed her and the boarding house as his emergency contact. Certainly, a man in his position could understand – she had a house full of boarders expecting dinner. The way she saw it, William and Paul, while nice young men, were not her relations and, ultimately, not her problem. And there was no way on God's green earth she could be held responsible for this double pack of trouble that had landed in her lap. She helped where she could, but she had limits, after all. Surely, he understood.

The woman had drawn an unwavering line. It didn't seem to matter what he said. He didn't care at that point how bad his unwillingness to help his nephews sounded. Enough was enough. The boys were not related to him by blood. He did all he could to persuade Marge Goodbody to care for the boys. He thought there might still be time to head this situation off before Alice could hear about it.

Marge, however, was undeterred by any of his rationalizations. She'd been in similar situations too many times and could play the guilt card with expertise. Surely, Alice and Cyrus, as aunt and uncle by blood and marriage, would want to aid their innocent nephews in their time of need. As a gesture of goodwill, Marge threw in that she'd do what she could to help with Paul, but only until other arrangements could be made. That was her final offer.

Once again, Cyrus knew he was beaten. He'd been bested by three women in less than a week, a sure sign he was slipping. On some level, he knew what Alice would say. He was more afraid of what she might do. There was risk for him however the situation played out. He was not about to lose his wife and marriage over the fates of a couple of skinny-neck punks.

"Listen, lady," Cyrus tried again half-politely. "I've got trains to deal with, and I don't have time for this right now. Will you do me one more favor? Please call my wife at home. She can figure this out. Tell her I'll pick up William from the hospital as soon as I can."

Finally satisfied the matter would be resolved, Marge Goodbody agreed and bid Cyrus goodnight. One more phone call, and she was off the hook. It had been a close call.

* * *

Alice Ligon had been on the phone nonstop. After Marge Goodbody called and relayed the arrangements she'd made with Cyrus, Alice got a call from the mortuary. After assuring her that they were in possession of Billie's body, they explained that Alice had been listed as next of kin on the paperwork. They were calling to determine if the family had made plans for a funeral.

In fact, she'd called her mother, Ida, and her sister Dorothy in Washington and then reached her sister Wilma in Illinois. It would take the family several days to assemble. In the meantime, Billie's body would have to be brought back to rest in the Ligons' parlor. There was no way around it. The funeral home was unable to accommodate Billie's body unless there were plans for them to hold a funeral service there. While they understood that the family was grieving, certainly, she could understand they were running a business, after all. Later, the newspaper called, wanting to verify the details that would be printed in the paper.

"Oh, good Lord!" she cried after hanging up the phone for the last time that day. "If this isn't God's wrath, I don't know what is!"

* * *

William looked around the parlor as if in a fog. He'd spent the last several days there with the Ligons and was beginning to recuperate. He'd arrived from the hospital after the accident to find his mother's body laid out in the Ligons' parlor, her skin white as a ghost. She'd been there for nearly a week now, waiting on the relations to come so she could be buried.

The day had finally arrived. The house was crowded with relations and warm under the circumstances. They would be headed out for the service and burial shortly. William looked down at the cast around his leg and wondered how he was going to manage. Cyrus and Alice Ligon had been kind to somehow find room for him, but they had drawn the line with Paul. There was simply no room to spare. After Alice had explained the situation and offered to pay Marge Goodbody, she was finally able to get her to extend Paul's stay the extra few days at the boardinghouse until extended family would arrive to pick him up. As it was, William had slept toe to head in Helen's bed with her, his broken leg and all.

He caught sight of Paul coming in the front door; his brother had just arrived from the boarding house for the services. The two sets of eyes met, one brother searching the other for clues to their respective fates. Both shook their heads, and neither uttered a word.

Before the day was out, William had met more relations than he'd ever known he had. It served to briefly interrupt the overwhelming grief and pain he felt. The two brothers were escorted by a small subset of family members to Billie's graveside to witness her final rites.

William bowed his head during the prayer, saw his foot in a cast, and flashed to his accident. It was a little awkward, but he managed to navigate in and out of the cemetery okay. At least his leg didn't hurt as much as his heart did. His life was upside down for sure.

After the burial, the Ligons hosted a reception back at their house, and the brothers learned their fate. Family would care for them, but they were to be split up. Paul was to go to live with Aunt Opal in Chicago, Illinois. He'd be leaving the following day. William was to head for Camas, Washington, to live with his aunt Dorothy and uncle Odmund Egaas, along with his grandmother Ida, who'd moved from Arkansas to join them in Camas some time back.

Aunt Dorothy Potter, photo from Little Rock, Arkansas, announcement about wedding: "Mrs. Odmund Egaas Weds in WA." Dorothy and Odmund took in William after Billie's death.

"Remember when I mentioned my grandmother Billie came from a good-sized family?" my aunt interrupted herself to ask me.

"I remember," I dutifully replied.

"Dorothy Potter Egaas was Billie's oldest sister. From my cousin Helen's perspective, Dorothy was considered a superstar by the family at large."

"Oh?" I responded inquisitively.

"According to Helen, there wasn't anything Dorothy couldn't do well. She was an attractive woman with a good head on her shoulders and an honor graduate of Little Rock high school. She received her A.B. degree from Arkansas College at Batesville and was listed as a member of Beta Sigma Omicron, a national sorority. Evidently, Aunt Dorothy had made quite a name for herself as a singer and actor in the local theater prior to her leaving Little Rock. Cousin Helen spoke of her with great reverence, as if she were in a class of her own, clearly a Little Rock celebrity."

"I think I remember her from the pictures you showed me."

"She married my uncle Odmund Egaas in 1934 in Camas, Washington. He was an executive with Crown-Willamette Paper Company at that point in their lives. My cousin Helen recounts wailing aloud when she was finally informed that her beloved cousin William would be moving so far away. She was pacified by Aunt Dorothy that day, who said that if she kept up her schoolwork and behaved herself, perhaps her parents would allow her to visit William in Washington."

"I've got to side with your cousin Helen on this one, Aunt Joni. That is one hell of a heartbreaking story. I think about that really, really old photo of Grandpa Bill as a happy, super-healthy-looking baby. It's gut-wrenching to think about what he went through with his brother Paul!" I concluded with the shock of it all still registering on my face.

My aunt wore her own painfully sad expression, but she didn't respond.

I knew from the years I'd spent listening to my dad's horror stories about my grandfather Bill that the damage done to him from all of it was quite literally mentally and physically real. He had stuffed it all way down inside to survive the extraordinary pain it evoked for him. Predictably, as the decades flew by, the pain continued to manifest through the entire family with devastating results. The crazy-making part about it was that while no one could identify

Grandpa Marvin Fountain with WJW in Camas, Washington. Fountain was Ida Potter's second husband.

what was going on with William, his periodically seriously abusive behavior was obvious for everyone to see and feel.

It also became crystal clear for me at that moment why these *Tales* and those my aunt has yet to release needed to see the light of day. These horrifically abusive cycles among human beings, among extended family, must be interrupted. Awareness and knowledge, together with action, lead to peace of mind for everyone – and huge positive change in the world.

My aunt interrupted my train of thought to remind me there was one new set of developments that had been waiting its turn to unfold. As she'd hinted earlier, it was related to the shooting.

"I'm sorry, Aunt Joni. I was a million miles away. You were trying to tell me there was one more leg to this part, weren't you? But for the love of God, what else could have happened at this point?"

"I know. That's how I felt when I read this last article your brother sent from his most recent findings. So, to put this all into context, Billie died on May 3, 1935, roughly a month shy of two years after the shooting."

"That helps give me a time frame for the point William and Paul got separated."

"This last incident occurred about two months after Billie died," my aunt said, letting out a long sigh. "We owe a debt of gratitude to your brother, GenealogyBank, and the *Arkansas Gazette* once again, for without all of their efforts, it looks like we would not have learned that Grace Gordon suffered life-threatening injuries at the hands of our family not just once, but most likely twice. The least we can do now is extend our sincerest apologies and condolences to her and her family for the suffering she endured, none of which she deserved."

"Wait a minute, Sherlock. Wasn't the woman's name Grace Medley?" I asked her. "And what the hell else happened to her?" I added before she had a chance to respond.

"Yes, you have it right. It was Mrs. Grace Medley who was shot three times by Grandma Billie. Fast forward two years, and she'd been divorced. She was listed as Miss Grace Gordon in this last article, which referenced the prior incident in which she'd been shot."

"And my second question?" I asked, not really giving her much of a chance to finish her train of thought as my mind impatiently began to whirl on what she'd just been sharing and what else could have possibly happened. I realized it must have had something to do with Murphy.

"Grace Gordon fell out of the front passenger seat of a car headfirst onto the street, and the car sped away. She suffered a fractured jaw and a possible fractured skull. There were three eyewitnesses sitting out on their porches that July 12 evening who agreed on what they saw. Unfortunately, it was too dark at that point for them to get a license plate number."

"Oh, my God," I replied. "That is outrageous! Did you learn anything else from the article?"

"Yes, there were some other details provided. One of the witnesses attempted to run after the car and gave up after he'd chased it a block or so. Not long after that, the witnesses waved down another car that came by, and the two men in that car, who must have been given a rough description of the vehicle, headed off to see if they could chase it down."

"Did they catch up to the guy?"

"Evidently, they caught up to someone, another innocent person ensnared by this ugly web. An officer was called to the scene, and the African American man in that car, along with the officer and the two men who'd given chase, all returned to the scene of the original crime. At that point, the three witnesses and another officer there were clear that the man who'd been chased down was not at all involved in that crime, and he, thank God, was released."

"Wow! They must have gotten enough of a glimpse of the driver to know the difference!"

"I came to the same conclusion. The article went on to briefly and inaccurately describe Billie shooting Grace, and it mentioned that Billie was dead."

"What did they get wrong?" I asked, curious to see if there might be any new light shed by the press two years after the event.

"I suspect that the journalist must have written the article in a rush and didn't fact check what they'd written. For starters, the time frame was off by a year; the article said that the shooting had happened about a year ago, when it was really two. It stated that Grace was critically wounded when Billie shot at Vera, who was with Murphy, the former city fireman, and the bullet missed its mark and hit Grace."

"I see what you mean. It suggests there was only one shot! What the hell, Aunt Joni! What's the probability that the man behind that wheel wasn't Murphy?"

"Slim to none would be my first guess, I hate to say," she replied. "But given there's an ex-husband involved, we'd probably better make that fifty-fifty."

"What do you think happened?"

"Murphy got wind that Billie had passed on, and he came back to Little Rock. My cousin Helen Potter Mashburn was direct with me years ago that he didn't stay away long. However, neither she nor William appeared to know anything about this last incident with Grace. William would have already moved to Camas by then, and Helen may have been too young to be reading the papers. As for Murphy, he may have come back as soon as he knew the coast was clear with my grandmother Billie's death."

"He probably kept in touch with Vera, wouldn't you think?" I asked her.

"Yep. The two were clearly in cahoots. As for Grace Gordon, I'm afraid she was the one person who was a danger to them because of what she knew."

"What do you mean?"

"Their greatest worry would have been that Grace had figured out – or maybe Vera told her – that Vera and Murphy had hired the hitman that made the attempt on Billie's life. Grace Gordon must have known that Murphy and Vera were having an affair; she would have also known Vera was lying when she claimed to the police and reporters that she and Murphy were only friends. If Murphy, Vera, or Grace had been called to the stand under oath about who hired the hitman against Billie and why, they all would have had to lie their way through it."

"I see what you mean."

"So, Grandpa Murphy headed back to Little Rock and hooked back up with Vera. The two of them got to talking, probably started drinking, and began to assess the situation. Perhaps Vera had gotten wind of Grace talking to somebody about it. Maybe it contributed to her divorce in some manner. Perhaps her husband didn't want to participate in a cover-up. Or perhaps Grace had fought with Vera over keeping quiet. The question had to come up: was Grace Gordon still a risk to them? I think it's fair to say the damage she could have done to them by talking to somebody else about it may have already occurred by the time he got back. Given the circumstances, Murphy and Vera had more than a bit of motive in the situation."

"It does seem strange that Grace would have been divorced after getting shot. It would have taken her some time to recover from the gunshot wounds to the chest, I'd think."

"Tragedy has been known to spawn more of the same, I'm afraid. In fairness, it's not unheard of for couples to split up after major life events – the loss of a child, for example, or an accident with life-threatening injuries."

"So, explain to me how she could have gone headfirst to the street?" I said, cringing at the thought of getting pushed out of a car.

"Murphy and Vera must have agreed to set a date with Grace to get together for old times' sake, to have a drink to their health and toast surviving Billie's barrage of bullets. One round led to another, and another, and another. It's hard to say what Grace might have shared with them under the influence. Whatever it was, it must have confirmed for Murphy that she continued to pose a risk to them. It's not clear if they were trying to actually kill her or give her a near-lethal warning. I cannot imagine how anyone could go head first out of a car to the street unless they were severely inebriated or otherwise unconscious. Sadly, I'd guess Vera was seated in the middle, with Grace leaning against the door. The rest is obvious."

"That's just sick!" I cried, springing up from the bench. "Oh, my God! Was Murphy ever held accountable for any of it?"

"Not to my knowledge. As I mentioned, my father was so ashamed by what he did know that he never would have shared it, but then cousin Paula, my uncle Paul's daughter, helped us crack the lid on the original family story. The full drama took another twenty years to surface, with your brother's excellent assistance in the proverbial eleventh hour."

"Un-fucking-believably amazing! Now I totally get how difficult it has been for you to share all this, Aunt Joni. I guess the silver lining for me in hearing it all is that Murphy makes me feel pretty damn law-abiding by comparison."

"Perspective does make a difference, doesn't it?" My aunt rose from her chair. "I think our mission is accomplished for this evening."

CHAPTER 18

Alcohol and Power over Others Winding down the Trail

I slept late the next morning, and if I recall, we didn't rush to do much of anything that day. I was still processing everything I'd heard and learned during our last exchange. The effort from the night before had left us both with a lot to think about.

"Would you care for some coffee?" Aunt Joni asked me as I walked into the kitchen.

"That sounds good. Thanks!" I replied gratefully. Aunt Joni appreciated her coffee as much as I did. She'd been drinking decaf for some time, given her health issues, but when scientists finally determined caffeinated coffee was better than decaffeinated for reducing heart disease, she had partially switched back to a higher test brew. It was a delicate balance, given her takotsubo syndrome and neurological condition.

"Any thoughts about our efforts from last evening?" Aunt Joni said as she filled my mug, interrupting my musing.

"I'd be blinder than a bat to miss the obvious themes in our family. I am struck by the combination of alcohol addiction and violence in this story, that has left a brutally long trail of evidence." I found myself flinching as I replied, and I shook my head.

"I agree with you," she replied. "It's not surprising that we've been unable to look back through the fog of inebriation to attempt to understand it, given the depth and prevalence of the disease in the human condition."

As my aunt sipped her coffee, I reflected on the fact that my father and every one of his five siblings, including Aunt Joni, were all born alcoholics. Their parents, William and Eloise, Grandfather Murphy, Great-Grandfather Junius, and Great-Great-Great-Grandfather Burwell had all been under the influence of alcohol a good majority of their waking days. Heart disease is a likely outcome for children born of active and ancestral alcoholics. Our family tells these tales all too well.

"Aunt Joni, growing up with alcoholism entrenched in our family has given both of us a pretty potent perspective, one dreadfully convincing enough to know better, wouldn't you say? Think about how many without that experience might be fooled into thinking their drinking won't get the better of them. Shit, it's a problem even for those of us who do know better."

My aunt shook her head in agreement. "I'm thankful you and your brother each found your own way to truly relish sobriety. I've shared with you that the alcoholism in our family was obvious to me even as a child. It took me decades to understand the greater ramifications. It is an insidious disease that is actively passed from one generation to the next, affecting all levels of our being and capacity."

"Or, more likely, incapacity," I offered in return.

"That about says it all. I suspect very few can get through life without at least a glimpse of the fleeting pleasures of alcohol and its most debasing ugliness. Under the influence, judgment is suspended. Aggression and violence are more likely, while ethics and values are obliterated."

"You can say that again," I responded, shaking my head as I recalled hangovers I'd had along the way, not to mention the bullshit I'd engaged in and seen others pull while shit-faced drunk.

"Here's the hard truth about all of this," Aunt Joni declared. "An unthreatened, sober, and reasonably sane individual can recognize right from wrong, honest from dishonest, and, when presented with enough evidence, true from false and fact from fiction. And they can usually recognize it regardless of their prior exposure to religion, race, creed, color, gender identity, or sexual orientation."

"Heave-ho! Bravo, Aunt Joni! You go!" I responded earnestly.

"It is not right to enslave one another," she continued. "It is not right to harm another, unprovoked by the threat of violence. It is not okay to invade someone's personal, physical, or psychic private space without their permission – and certainly not for political, religious, or financial gains."

"So, how the hell could members of our family have held slaves for decades?" I asked her. Without giving her a chance to respond, I added, "How could our family fight one another in the Civil War? That's crazy!"

"I agree. How could my great-great-grandfather have started two families simultaneously and then skipped out on both of them? How could my grandfather have hired a hitman to murder my grandmother? How could Grandmother Billie have believed revenge would improve their family situation? It's all pretty crazy-making, is what it is."

"Aunt Joni, I still don't understand how our family could steal from one another and others over countless generations. It just makes me shudder with shame. But then, as I think about it, it really begs the ultimate question. How could either of us have gone the bulk of our lives without being aware of most of this?"

Aunt Joni sat in silence for a moment. "We know power over others has taken many forms. Religious organizations, political sovereigns, and even the Boy Scouts of America have all been guilty of using their power to control, manipulate, and sexually abuse the men, women, and children to whom they are purportedly responsible. It is perhaps easier for us to identify it in hindsight than to acknowledge it in real time in our lives, much less our own family. Killing someone or abusing them in any way in the name of any god with the aim of power over others is the ultimate definition of insanity and insult to reason."

"Breaking all these cycles, do you really think it's possible?" I asked, still in shock at the enormity of the effort she, and now we, had undertaken. "And isn't ignorance supposed to be bliss?"

"Having known ignorance and now sensing some enlightenment, you tell me," she replied.

"I'd say ignorance is seriously misrepresented as bliss. It seems to me we human beings like to find ways to let ourselves off the hook, don't we?"

My aunt smiled and silently nodded.

CHAPTER 19

Go West, W.J. Honey, Go West!

"So, William moved from Little Rock to the state of Washington?" I asked her after a good, long day of rest and relaxation.

"Yes, he did. His aunt and uncle, Dorothy and Odmund Egaas, were both teachers and clearly understood that William needed some tender loving care and direction in his life. Thankfully, William had landed in sound hands. Before long, he was enrolled right into high school!"

"I don't understand. Had he even finished junior high school?" I asked her.

"No, he never did. I asked him the same question when I was a kid. Evidently, his circumstances were considered special. He had shown himself to be capable of high school material, so he was allowed to pass ninth grade with a waiver. Remember, Dorothy and Odmund were well connected within the school system. Besides, the baseball team at the high school had a spot all lined up for him!"

"No kidding?"

"It didn't take him long to prove himself on the ball field, either. He played shortstop most often, as he was quick on his feet. Sometimes he played third base. And he could hit the ball." She paused to take a sip of her beverage. "When asked, my father would reply he had a .300 batting average during his years playing baseball. That's pretty good!"

"That is impressive," I replied, nodding.

"Long story short, William excelled at baseball, attracting the attention of pro ball scouts looking for promising young talent. Eventually, he was playing high school ball by day and minor league pro ball in the off hours. William got to do a fair amount of traveling with his minor league club and earned himself some money in the process."

"That's pretty cool."

"My dad really loved baseball. Having known them both, I suspect his aunt Dorothy and uncle Odmund had something to do with him applying to Willamette University, in Salem, Oregon."

"Why so?"

"They were in a position to realize how vital it was for individuals to continue to learn and expand their mental capacities, how it was truly a gift to have the opportunity to pursue higher education. He was accepted and awarded a full scholarship to play for the Willamette University baseball team."

"Wow, that's impressive!"

"Your father shared with me his earliest memories of life with our parents. He remembered William showing him a black and white picture of himself in a very nice yellow convertible. Michael

1941 Willamette baseball team; William Whitmore is in the front row, left.
Courtesy Willamette University Archives and Special Collections, Salem, Oregon.

figured that Dad had to have made some money playing baseball – enough to buy himself that car. It may have been his first, and he evidently drove it from Camas, Washington, down to Salem, Oregon, to start school there."

"That's quite an image," I replied, my mind's eye seeing myself making the trip down I-5 with the top down.

"I'm not sure about the rest of that car story," my aunt continued. "Curiously, however, William made a point to share with me years later that he'd watched many a man who'd ruined his life with his automobile obsessions. He seriously cautioned me over making too much about them – that a car was basically something to get you from one side of town to the other. It was an important lesson he'd learned, and one I didn't forget."

"That's a different perspective," I offered. I was old enough to appreciate the sums required to buy a new car or have to maintain it. "It makes me think about my dad's Alpha Romeo that's been in the garage all these years." We hadn't been able to let it go.

"Michael also mentioned that the conditions of William's athletic scholarship precluded him from getting paid for playing professional minor league ball. He seemed to imply that Dad must have done some fancy footwork to continue playing ball and keep his scholarship, perhaps even playing under an alias, suggesting he was possibly living a dual life. One of my Boston friends tried to find William in the minor league rosters for those years but turned up no players with his given name. It's possible that he was forced to stop. I do recall him telling me he'd gotten a job that first year at a gas station near the campus to help pay his bills."

"What an interesting riddle," I offered back, a bit puzzled as she nodded.

"And that's as good a spot as any for us to rest for the night. We covered plenty of miles last night," she declared with a sad smile. "It's okay that we took a break today."

Oh, my God, did we ever, I thought to myself, shaking my head.

William working at a gas station in Salem, Oregon, to help pay for school, 1941–1942

CHAPTER 20

The Bill and Eloise Story

"So," my Aunt Joni shared with me, prompted by our morning cups of coffee, "one winter morning in early February of 1942, William walked into a Salem, Oregon, coffee shop not far off the Willamette campus to get a bite to eat before class. There he spied Eloise Winn for the first time. William slid into a booth and began to examine the menu. As Eloise approached the table, he offered up a smile and found himself delighted to receive one from her in return."

★ ★ ★

"Good morning! How can I help you?" she asked him cheerfully.

"Good morning, ma'am! How 'bout some peach pie and coffee?" he responded.

"No problem!" She turned over his cup. "Cream?"

"Yes, please, ma'am."

When she returned with his pie and coffee, she couldn't help but ask him where he was from. It wasn't every day that a Southern drawl came breezing through the Willamette Valley.

"I've just moved down here from Camas, Washington, ma'am."

"With that drawl? You're kidding, right?" she responded incredulously.

William found himself getting a bit nervous with Eloise. He liked her already and didn't want to blow his introduction. "Oh, I was born and raised in Little Rock, Arkansas, ma'am. I can't he'p it!" he added, shaking his head and flashing her a sheepish grin, which produced an immediate burst of laughter from Eloise.

"Okay, Mr. Little Rock. Do you have a name?"

"My name's William, ma'am. William Whitmore." He extended his hand.

"Eloise," she responded, shaking his hand. "Eloise Winn. It's a pleasure to meet you, William."

* * *

"During their introduction that morning, William learned quite a bit about this petite brunette. She was a fourth-generation Oregonian – an official "Mossback," she'd declared herself – from covered-wagon, pioneer stock. A Willamette University sophomore, she was a full year ahead of him in school. He was impressed to hear Willamette had awarded Eloise an academic scholarship and that her pay from the café covered the cost of her books and supplies."

"That's how they met, huh? Just like that?" I interjected.

"Just like that. Cut to the chase, William was quite taken with Eloise, one might say smitten on the spot, and he summoned up the courage to invite her to the Valentine's Day dance!"

"She accepted?"

"Nope. As the story goes, she turned him down – at least initially. However, William was not deterred. He persisted over that week, and eventually, she consented to accompany him to the dance. That was February, mind you."

"What? What happened?"

"That dance must have been an enjoyable one for both of them. As far as I know, William had never had a steady girlfriend prior to then. The pair began a whirlwind, two-month courtship and got married April 26, 1942, in Stevenson, Washington, before returning to campus to finish out their spring semester." My aunt stretched in her seat.

"So, they eloped, eh? Two months later? That was a pretty fast dance," I noted for the record.

"Neither William nor Eloise returned to college that fall. Your father, Michael, was conceived by June. It's not clear what else might have driven their decision to simultaneously drop out of college, get married, and have children. However, I can tell you World War II had begun, and it was possible to get a draft deferral if one was the sole supporter of a family with dependents."

"That explains quite a bit!" I exclaimed aloud. "That makes my dad an early-edition Baby Boomer!"

"That's right. Michael Winn Whitmore was born on February 20, 1943, a year to the week after William and Eloise first met. Eloise gave birth to their second child, Patricia, two years later. And we do know William worked on military assignment for a short while at the Portland shipyard. He had one picture he'd kept of himself in his work uniform. Years later, when people asked William why he quit his baseball career, he unfailingly blamed the Japanese."

"Did they ever go back to finish college?"

"No, they never went back for their degrees. However, their lifelong learning was still very much underway!" she explained. "This portion of William's life has some familiar echoes to it."

"What do you mean?" I found myself asking her for the millionth time.

"They were living in downtown Salem in a community of one-story brick rentals called 'The Courts.' According to brother Michael, Mom and Dad had the far-back unit, which had access to a small garden plot facing the alley. William, who preferred to be called 'Bill' at that point in his life, and Eloise managed a grocery store at the end of the same block, which was very convenient for them."

"I remember my dad pointing out The Courts to me as we drove through Salem one day," I recalled aloud.

"Some of Michael's earliest childhood memories came flooding back to him when we talked about it. He remembered being very young and seemingly fearless, running around naked as a jaybird and spending the day in a galvanized washtub full of cool water to find relief from the heat of summer. And that jibes with an often-told family story that has a buck-naked Michael twice managing to escape their house, toddling away from the garden and down the sidewalk to the corner store, where he proceeded to do his 'business' outside the front door of the establishment!"

"What a hilarious story!" I laughed.

"That small garden was evidently a powerful place for Michael's young memory. Seeds were planted that grew roots to survive his lifetime. During our last conversation, he recalled his first and only memory of meeting our grandfather Murphy."

"He met Murphy?" I asked in disbelief.

"Michael remembered Murphy visiting them at The Courts. Murphy walked Michael out to the little garden plot Eloise maintained near the alley. There the two of them sat down together. Murphy took out a pocketknife and cut them each a green onion. Michael watched as his grandfather salted and licked the top of his hand and then munched the green onion. Then Murphy handed Michael a freshly cut green onion and the saltshaker so he could try for himself."

★ ★ ★

"They're better with salt," Murphy explained to Michael.

★ ★ ★

"Michael relayed that he could still picture sitting there with Murphy as if it were yesterday. A short time later, the two sauntered back inside. The memory was complete, with Eloise proclaiming the two of them reeked of green onions."

"Was there more to this meeting with Murphy?" I asked her.

"I asked Michael the same question," she replied, smiling. "He estimated he was maybe four or five and described Murphy in detail from memory as midsize in height, very tan, skinny, and quite nice. Michael remembered him as a gentle man, whom he sensed loved him and his sister Pat." She paused for a moment before continuing. "Many years later, my father shared a very different set of disturbing memories from that visit with his father," she added, frowning.

"What was that?" I asked her, my eyebrows rising in anticipation of what the hell might come next.

"William didn't talk much about his father. His memories were not particularly positive. He relayed to me that his father had tracked him and Paul to Oregon and that he'd come to mooch from them. He evidently didn't stay very long. During that visit, William's entire set of autographed baseball cards went missing. He was certain Murphy had stolen them."

"That's awful!" I exclaimed.

"It made my father heartsick to talk about it. William had met many baseball greats in his years playing ball. He talked about Pee-Wee Reese the most – they were only a couple of years apart in age. Pee-Wee played for the Dodgers when they were still in Brooklyn, and Dad met him and others while playing for one of the farm teams. I remember asking him why Murphy would have stolen the cards. My father winced, rattled off all the signatures he'd managed to collect in the years he'd played ball, and explained that the cards had increased in value as the greats of baseball had passed. His father, Murphy, was just about a homeless inebriate by that point..." Her voice trailed off for a moment.

"My dad intimated he believed Murphy learned of his baseball card collection and had come with the intent to steal them. To my knowledge, it might have been the last time William saw his father," she concluded.

"God, that's sad!" I remember exclaiming. As I sat with everything she shared, I realized there was new information. "But wait a minute – you hadn't mentioned that his brother, Paul, was in Oregon," I pointed out to her, somewhat confused.

"I didn't know it myself!" she responded. "I hadn't been born yet. Michael remembered Paul came to stay with them quite a bit at The Courts and eventually had his own place in Salem. He worked at a Chevron station in south Salem, across town. So, at some point, Paul must have left Chicago and followed William to Salem. Michael did relay memories of Paul as a vibrant soul who loved life. He remembered him as a philosopher of sorts who evidently loved to engage Eloise in extemporaneous discussions. At one point, Michael, still a young boy, asked Uncle Paul about the meaning of life."

"Oh? What did Uncle Paul say to that?"

"Michael's question was met with guffaws from the adults. Then Uncle Paul acknowledged it was an intelligent question and seemed truly tickled that Michael had asked him."

I nodded and smiled, unsure what I'd say if a young child had the audacity to ask me such a thing.

"There was another truly tragic memory Michael shared with me from his childhood at The Courts," she said, pausing a moment to sip her beverage.

"What was that?" I prompted her as I began searching my brain for memories that might have fit such a description.

"Michael had made a friend in their neighborhood, and the two very young boys had begun to play from time to time on the sidewalk that lined the block. That block had a section where the sidewalk passed over Mill Creek underneath. The boys eventually gravitated down the sidewalk toward the creek. They hung their ribcages over the fence bar, absorbed by the sight and sound of the rushing waters below. Propelled to investigate further, they scooted themselves under the railing and climbed down the hill a short way to the creek bed. Mill Creek was running high and fast that late-fall day. Michael watched as his friend fell into the rushing waters and quickly disappeared from view."

"Oh, God! What happened?"

"Michael ran back to The Courts to find his father. Crying and shaking, he managed to get out that they'd been playing and his friend had fallen in the creek. Father and son returned to the site where the two boys had been exploring. It didn't take William long to find the boy's drowned body, trapped by a culvert screen a short distance downstream."

"That's really sad," I offered quietly.

"It must have been a traumatic experience for father and son, I'd guess. I can only imagine how devastated the parents of the other boy must have been."

"That would have been heartbreaking and difficult for all of them to forget."

"Your father did remember our parents as party types from his earliest memories," she continued. "I suspect Eloise and Bill may have done a fair amount of partying during college, as is typical for young adults. Evidently, they continued partying with their friends after leaving Willamette. Michael said he woke up one morning to find the house in disarray, with beer bottles covering every available surface. Bill and Eloise were still conked out from the party the night before. The trouble was, Michael and little sister Pat were hungry, and there was no milk left in the house."

"So, what did they do?" I asked her.

"I asked him the same question. Michael said he got out two bowls, poured cereal in each of them, and topped the cereal with beer they collected from bottles left around the room!"

"That's unbelievable," I replied, making a face.

"I have to agree with you. However, Michael sheepishly replied, as kids, they thought it was pretty cool, adding extra fizz to their snap, crackle, and pop!"

It struck me with the force of a California earthquake that my father's life had literally been framed by alcohol from one end to the other. I heard my aunt, as if from miles away, tell me that it was a perfect point for us to get refreshments before continuing.

"There was another significant memory that Michael shared of Eloise and Bill's time together at Willamette University," she told me afterward. "But this one, he heard about years later. Michael recalls he was studying landscape architecture at that point at OHSU, and he enjoyed a visit from Eloise and Pat."

"Oh? What happened?" I asked her, curious about what a "significant" memory might amount to on the William Whitmore and Eloise Winn family radar.

"They were exiting the Hatfield Building when Michael spied a picture of the building namesake, Mark Hatfield, in his capacity as dean of Willamette University. Hatfield would later serve as governor and as one of Oregon's longest-tenured US senators," she patiently explained to me. "He also attended Willamette University. It turns out he was just a bit older than Eloise and Bill, a couple of years ahead of them."

"That's fascinating! Quite a few of the largest Black Lives Matter protests that went on in Portland happened in front of the Hatfield Courthouse. So, I take it the two of them knew him at Willamette?" I asked her, now knowing for sure there were more tentacles to this tale than I could imagine.

"You raise a significant historical juncture of time and space, my dear one! You're probably aware by now that Oregon was the only state to enshrine a 'whites only' clause in the state constitution?"

"I am aware of that, yes, and it's just frickin' amazing to me!"

"That racist clause was removed from Oregon's constitution the same year Hatfield was elected the state's youngest governor ever."

"Huh. I didn't realize that. I suppose that was no coincidence."

"Back to your other question, Michael asked Eloise as they passed his photo that day if the family rumor about Mark Hatfield was true."

"What rumor was that?"

"Remember the Valentine's Day dance William bugged Eloise to attend?"

"Yeah." I nodded. "Was there something else you didn't mention before?"

"Mark Hatfield was evidently there. He and Eloise had previously been an item. Upon seeing her in the company of another man, Hatfield evidently tried to put the move on her, and William exploded in a rage of jealously, decking him right there and then," she added with eyebrows raised.

"So, the rumor Michael heard was true?" I asked her.

"Eloise nodded her assent to Michael, with our sister Pat as a witness, the afternoon of their visit. So, yes, the rumor was confirmed by Eloise to be true."

"Why am I sensing there's more to this tale with Hatfield?" I asked her, still not sure what I was cluing in to.

"Your senses are functioning," she responded. "That's a good sign. And yes, it's true. Ironically, Hatfield figures into our family *Tales* in all three volumes."

Her confirmation that my senses were honing in on something was helpful for me to hear. Before now, when insight or intuition had occurred to me, I'd never given any thought to where the hell it came from; I'd just been glad to have had some.

"Your father witnessed repeated incidents of your grandpa Bill's explosive temper and jealousy over Eloise and other men," she continued. "Many years later, William punched someone on the Salem golf course for intimating Eloise had an abortion her first year while at Willamette! William didn't deny it, but he did once try to explain to me that it was his way of defending her honor." She shook her head.

There was a pause before she continued. I knew there was more that would come out. I had a better sense by that point of when she was up for it and when she'd had enough. She always seemed to know with me, I must tell you.

"I know there's more you want to talk about regarding all the questions that have gotten stirred for you, my dear nephew. And that's okay. We've gotten through everything we need to cover for now about the Whitmore family history. And we'll pick up where we've just left off with our William and Eloise tale in volume two from the perspective of the Winn ancestors."

"That's really helpful, Aunt Joni. I was wondering what that juncture of past, present, and future was going to look like! I started keeping a list some time ago of the questions as they come up for me, and there are more than a few. However, they can all wait until this evening!"

Once our morning routines were accomplished, we gathered our gear and headed out to the back nine holes of the golf course for the afternoon. They were Aunt Joni's favorites. I couldn't argue, even though they were much tougher than the front half of the course. Thankfully, my game had gradually improved. I was looking forward to being outside and playing in the sunshine. It really helped both of us, it was obvious to see.

Eloise Winn, as a first-year Willamette University student, Salem, Oregon, 1940–1941.

William and Eloise eloped and were married on April 26, 1942, in Stephenson, Washington.

Eloise Winn Whitmore, sitting on the steps at The Courts, in Salem, Oregon, with son Michael, 1943.

Mike and sister Pat pushing dog in baby carriage in Salem, 1945–1946.

WJW with his children, Mike and Pat, at The Courts, in Salem, Oregon, circa 1945–1946.

Drums along the Mohawk at the Elsinore Theatre in Salem, Oregon. WJW (center) and Paul (right) with unidentified friend (left).

1940s Oregon coast photo with Eloise (left) and two friends.

Santa Claus with sister Patricia Whitmore.

Oregon governor and longtime senator Mark Hatfield.

CHAPTER 21

Approaching the Edge

I had grown during my visits over the years with my aunt in ways that sometimes surprised me. I was more relaxed and confident, and I suppose it showed. I knew it was okay to ask her just about anything on my mind – even the toughest questions.

"I've heard enough of your story to know you've faced death more than once, Aunt Joni. Are you afraid to die?" I asked her that evening on the bench.

"When I was a child, the thought of dying triggered a feeling of terror that would make me sit straight up in bed. I had absolutely no context in which to understand it."

"And now?" I asked curiously.

"I'm relieved to say I no longer fear death, and I no longer expect it to be a point of total extinction like I did when I was a child. My perspective evolved rapidly. I lost six people close to me during my teenage years. When I met others my age who had never lost anyone dear to them, the differences in our perspectives on both life and death were obvious to me. But those revelations were eclipsed at that point by the profound hole that had been left in my life by the passing of those who'd mentored me along the way."

"I get that part," I offered, shaking my head.

"Now I'm paying attention to being as prepared as I can possibly be for the transition," she responded. "Someone I met decades ago shared with me a pearl on the topic I've never forgotten."

"What was that?"

"It's a reflection that has been helpful to me in many a situation. They shared that those on the edge can see both sides."

"That's powerful on lots of levels!"

"I've found it helpful. It speaks to removing blinders from our point of view that are created when we get overly attached to one side or the other."

I sat quietly. This was stuff I hadn't talked about much, and I had no idea what to say.

"I think the intensity of the grief we feel at the loss of loved ones is born from not wanting to let them go," she offered. "Imagine how horrifyingly painful it must have been for William and Paul to lose Billie. The intensity of the emotions caused by the death of a loved one is completely understandable. Those departed are seemingly gone forever. It's these powerful emotional attachments in life that become painfully obvious when they are torn away from us."

"I get that part," I replied with chagrin.

"My perspective about death continued to evolve over my lifetime. I've experienced a deepening connection with many friends and family after they've departed. There came a point when I realized I had more family and close friends on the other side of the veil than I have remaining in my life."

"Couldn't that just be your mind having a sentimental attachment to those folks?" I asked her, playing devil's advocate.

"I've been given precious examples that the veil between the worlds is very thin." She paused for a moment.

"Wow, Aunt Joni! That's fascinating. Will you elaborate?"

"Whether or not we're ready, a crack between the worlds sometimes appears. When we are ready for it, we can hear it, see it, dream it, sense it, feel it, and ultimately know it for what it is."

"You lost me somewhere along the way."

"When I was growing up, what I'm calling the crack between the worlds was generally referred to under the catchall category of extra-sensory perception, or ESP. In fact, the realm of our collective psyche and our ability to access it has been referred to in many ways over time. C.G. Jung named it the 'collective unconscious,' which was a huge breakthrough for the West and the science of psychology. He discovered that the mind contains memories and impulses that weren't formed in that individual's lifetime but are common to humanity as a whole, originating in the inherited structure of our brain. It's also referred to as the wisdom of perfect knowledge, the state of all-knowing intelligence. The Buddha wisdom."

"Okay, I'm getting a clue. Thank you, Aunt Joni, for your patience with me. You're talking about intuition, yeah?"

"Yes. Our individual psyche, the greater collective psyche, and the universal spirit are all connected. Literally. Occurrences of intuition convey information from the greater universe that becomes available as it passes through us via our true law nature to conscious awareness."

"What are you saying?" I asked her, not quite getting it. "What is our true law nature?"

"I'll circle back around to this in a bit. To satisfy you for now, it refers to the true nature of our existence."

"Okay. I'm seriously starting to understand you. That is huge for me and a little frightening, Aunt Joni! Meanwhile, I'm starting to connect the dots between all of these family history lessons and the brain I've inherited from all of our ancestors. We are literally a product of all of this history, aren't we?"

"You are truly getting the picture, nephew," Aunt Joni replied, sipping her water.

"So, will you say more about intuition while we're still on the subject?" I prompted her.

"There are many types of intuition. Depending on the source, they'll tell you there are two, three, four, or even more than a dozen different types. When I began trying to understand intuitive and synchronistic experiences in my life that I couldn't explain, I was fortunate to get directed to Helen Palmer. I studied with her decades ago at what was then called the Center for the Investigation and Training of Intuition, which she founded and where she served as guide and mentor to many."

"You've mentioned her before," I responded encouragingly. "But can you give me an example of a few of the different types of intuition?"

"Let's start with this one: unhindered knowledge of the past, present, or future. Those fall under the umbrella of claircognizance. A claircognizant is one who has had an intuitive act of clear knowing."

"Okay, so I've heard of a clairvoyant before. What's their specialty?" I asked, starting to get a clue.

"Clairvoyance is the intuitive act of clear seeing."

"That helps and clues me in on the fact that these abilities correspond with our various natural senses, don't they?"

"That's right. So, here are a couple more. Take a rational guess," she encouraged me. "What is a clairaudient? Or a clairsentient?"

"I'd guess the first is an intuitive act of clear hearing?"

"So far, so good."

"I've heard there are folks who get an audible signal prior to earthquakes."

My aunt smiled at me, nodding. "And the second?"

"I'm stumped. Help me here. I'm bordering on overload."

"A clairsentient is an intuitive act of clear feeling. I've also heard it referred to as sensate intuition."

"So, like if someone were to get a tingling sensation across their skin."

"That's right. Just to be clear, we're talking about psychic conveyance via a physical sensation or feeling. We're not talking about emotional feelings."

"That makes sense. So, what about that family pain in the ass we were discussing earlier? That's not sensate intuition, is it?"

"No, it's not, although it's clearly an empathetic response from our central nervous system. And while it appears inherited, it is psychosomatic in response to something painful we've seen or heard. It's another example of our genetic inheritance that continues to manifest physiologically among our family."

"That's just crazy! I think I get the difference."

"To contrast, we all come equipped with multiple layers of these intuitive sensory abilities, and if any of them are active within us, often one type of intuition will be stronger or more active than the others. Palmer was also the child of two alcoholics, which made me intrigued to know what I might learn from her. She spoke with complexity about things that were entirely new to me yet in a way that was plain and simple to grasp. She shared wisdom meant to last lifetimes – and beyond."

"That's quite a coincidence, Aunt Joni. I get the sense you learned an awful lot from her."

"No kidding! I'd add it was more than a coincidence. The parallel of alcoholism in both of our families fits Jung's definition of a synchronicity to a tee!"

"Remind me again. What's the difference between a coincidence and a synchronicity?"

"Synchronicity is where there is a substantively meaningful connection between two seemingly otherwise causally unrelated yet parallel events in space and time. Jung provided endless examples from his studies of humanity. The classic one generally offered from his work is of a patient describing her dream of a scarab beetle. At the same moment, the pair heard a knock on the window. It was a scarab beetle."

"That is amazing! Wait a minute. Didn't you tell me there were synchronicities related to *Torch Time Tales*?"

"Yes, there is a growing number! Our longtime family friend Guy Goode, after being brought up to speed on the latest developments, suggested to me in the eleventh hour of this effort that this was a tale that apparently didn't want to end."

"That's quite an observation on his part. Interesting."

"I know I told you about the synchronicity of the timing of our audio production and the landmark decision of the Supreme Court awarding land in Oklahoma that had been promised to the Native Americans forced to march the Trail of Tears?"

"That rings a powerful bell, yes!" I responded, nodding.

"Okay, so did I have a chance to share your brother's recent discovery about the synchronicity between Grandfather Murphy and yours truly?"

"No!" I practically shouted. "That doesn't ring any bells! You've been holding out on me again!" I laughed. We had gone through this routine more than a few times over the years, as our respective research discoveries, and the timing of our visits to share them, were inevitably out of sync.

"Remember me mentioning Cousin Helen's observation that Murphy eventually returned to Little Rock?"

"Yep, I do. And?"

"Did I mention he was a golfer?"

"It rings a bell. Didn't Vera Hatch refer to golfing with Murphy during her interview at the police station?"

"Your memory is on target. Yes, she did."

"So, what about it?"

"Your brother found a newspaper article during my last visit, just before the pandemic broke out. Neither one of us had ever seen it before. Murphy had evidently hit a hole in one."

"No kidding! You had one in California, didn't you?"

"Yes, on the eleventh hole here. Get this. This one's a doubleheader!"

"Huh? Aren't you mixing metaphors between baseball and golf?"

"You ought to be used to it by now with my dyslexic sense of humor!" she added, poking fun at herself. "Murphy hit his hole in one on the eleventh hole of a golf course in Arkansas."

"Wow, that's extraordinary! I come back to your description of the cracks between the worlds, Aunt Joni, but that doesn't quite fit. This one's more like double-duty synchronistic ancestral morphic resonance!" I got Aunt Joni laughing with that one.

"Those synchronistic connections weren't the last of it!" she added. "Just before we were ready to call volume one complete, one of our editors discovered a website that allowed us to look up any famous relations we might have by our family name."

"What did that turn up?" I asked her.

"If it is to be believed, as we've not yet seen the kind of hard evidence we have with the rest of this Whitmore history, we are apparently related to Winston Churchill, the former prime minister of the United Kingdom, along with the late Princess Diana of Wales and her sons, Prince William and Prince Harry."

"No kidding? Just when I didn't think you could blow my mind any further, Aunt Joni. How many kings, princes and princesses, counts, and knights are we up to now?" I asked her, only half joking.

"I remarked to our producer, Robert Parish, after a recent major ancestral discovery on Mom's side, that what it said to me was that if someone or something that significant was still coming to light, who knows how much more we've totally missed that's directly related to the Whitmore or the Winn family stories! And then along comes Princess Diana, Prince William, Prince Harry, and Winston Churchill to add to the mix on the Whitmore side." She chuckled.

"Oh, my. That is fairly major, all right, Aunt Joni. Dare I ask, is that the end of the late-late-late-breaking developments?"

"No! I told you there's a list!" she said, still smiling. "This one gives me an enormous chuckle."

"Why so?"

"The editor I just mentioned had been holding out on us."

"Huh? Why so?"

"I'm not sure. These endeavors are a lot to get one's head around. It only took her a few months to get up to speed. I think the synchronicities between us were too amazing for her not to share!"

"Oh?" I asked delightedly, curious to hear what might emerge next. "And more than one?"

Joni nodded. "They came out one at a time. First, she shared that she has Norse relations. Another month passed, and she confessed to also having a synchronized birthdate and time just like my own!"

"Wow on both counts, I'd say. That's amazing! And you went to the same college, didn't you say?"

"Yes!"

"How did you meet her?"

"Do you remember me mentioning Christina Park, who helped me find the first-edition copies of the *Threefold Lotus Sutra*?"

"Oh, yeah. Didn't you conduct her admissions interview for Wellesley?"

"Yes, we had a wonderful conversation in Lakeport during her senior year in high school. I remember her being startled to learn that I understood some Sanskrit. Near the end of our time, after hearing a bit about my life and career, she finally asked me, 'Are all of you like this?' We both still chuckle over that first meeting."

"Well, Aunt Joni, you ought to be used to it by now. You are a bit of a freak, you know!" I said, gently poking fun at my aunt.

"I know," she replied, sighing. "And if the sins of my own mouth weren't a mile long, I might have gotten freakier even faster! Did you ever consider that possibility?"

"I hear you; I hear you. I've got the sins of my own mouth and mind to consider."

"Fast forward several years after she was admitted, and Christina asked me to mentor her after being selected for the inaugural class of presidential scholars; she was assigned to bring a focus of economic and social justice to all of her efforts."

"That sounds like quite an honor and quite a responsibility!" I added, impressed.

"I'd say so! To your question, Christina deserves credit for finding the editor I mentioned, among other helpful contributions to these efforts. I'm delighted and thankful to know them both."

"So, that explains that! Was that the end of the list of late-breakers?" I asked her, expecting at that point to get an affirmative response. I couldn't have been more wrong!

My Aunt Joni let out a long exhale with her reply. "No…"

"What do you mean, no?" I prompted when she didn't immediately continue.

"After all of those seriously late-breaking developments, the universe just had to serve up one last huge piece of this entire puzzle for me to include in the *Tales*."

"What was that?"

"It is the universe's way of helping me have a laugh at myself and my own ignorance! A cosmic giggle, if you will."

"Aunt Joni, you're talking in circles again. What are you saying? Speak plainly. Explain yourself!" I practically demanded.

"It was there for me to find at some point in my life, literally written in the stars to discover, but I had never gone there."

"What? What the heck are you trying to tell me now?" I said, beginning to feel myself get a little anxious all over again.

"Because I hadn't otherwise been able to find it for myself, the universe had to quite literally bring the evidence to me. It was delivered to me right here at this table, as a matter of fact."

"I'm sorry, Aunt Joni. I'm not following. You've lost me again!"

"With under ten days to go before our timeline, one of my longtime friends brought a friend of hers up for the weekend to meet me and get the tour of the place. That evening, after they arrived, the two of them were discussing their astrological star charts from an internet app on one of their smartphones when I sat down to join them."

"Had you ever looked at yours prior to that point?" I asked her.

"No, I never had. That's what I was trying to tell you. She wanted my birthdate and time and location, which I provided her."

"What did you learn?" I gently inquired when she didn't immediately respond.

"It was mind-blowing to discover, thanks to the help of my two friends and astro.com, that the astrological circumstances at the time of my birth were such as to have conveyed upon me *the gifts of intuition and a genuine concern for humanity at large.*"

"Wow! I'd say that fits the bill. What else?"

"I learned that I was on a particular spiritual mission with this lifetime and that I very much cherished my time alone in life, among other celestial particulars that I thought really nailed my description."

"Such as?"

"Such as that I really dislike continuous interruptions to my privacy!"

"Holy cow! Let me guess. Might continuously barking dogs fit that bill?" My aunt gave me the hairy eyeball and didn't respond. "So, was there more?" I prompted her.

"Yep. It relayed I would have many situations in life advising and counseling others, that I worked well with large groups and congregations and in business, and that I had a logical mind that picked up where others left off."

"Unbelievable! Was there more about your spiritual mission?"

"Evidently, I must pass a number of karmic tests of a mental character in order to return to my spiritual abode with a richer knowledge from this state of consciousness."

"That sounds like some heavy-duty celestial lifting there, Aunt Joni!" I offered, smiling.

"Not surprisingly, it relayed that by turning the mind inward, I would be able to know the world better by means of true self-knowledge."

"That sounds like it fits your bill to a tee!"

"You'll appreciate this after what you've seen around here; it also relayed that my mind actually feels the connections with nature and the higher aspects of things human."

"I see what you mean!" I responded, chuckling. "No kidding? What else?"

"Amazingly, it said that success will occur in my later years in life. Actually, I think it relayed success would be *beyond my mature years*," she added, laughing. "That part certainly fits! Importantly, it went on to relay that illuminating insights gleaned over my lifetime would allow me to connect my individuality with certain racial and family elements!"

"That's just out-of-this-world extraordinary! Dare I ask if there was anything more?"

"Yes! It commanded me to study those illuminating insights. If I were to do so, I would, perhaps, discover the spiritual mission destiny requires of me."

"Oh, my God, Aunt Joni! I see what you mean! Your star chart is literally speaking of the inspiration and creation of *Torch Time Tales*!"

"When I was able to read the text of all of this for myself, I have to say, even after everything I've been through, it was wonderful affirmation from the universe."

"I know you well enough now, Aunt Joni, that I'm going to ask you again: is there more to these astrological revelations?" I smiled and shook my head at her in amazement.

"Yes, importantly for *Torch Time Tales*, it relayed that if I could overcome my selfishness, I would accomplish my highest spiritual duties and my own degree of consciousness and perception will be expanded in the process."

"Oh, my God! Holy cow! What a mind-blower, Aunt Joni! Now you tell me!"

"My longtime friend sitting at the table, who'd been privy to hearing about my various endeavors, including the first *Torch Time Tales* volume, let out an 'oh, my God' herself and excitedly pointed out the parallels from the star charts with all of these efforts."

"Wow. You can say that again. *Oh, my God!*"

"This *is* what I'm supposed to be doing. It's celestially official!" Aunt Joni laughed. "Somehow, in the universal scheme of things, I feel like the last to be officially informed, but better late than never. I lamented to Guy Goode in our most recent phone call that I had not one academic credential in the world applicable to what I'm attempting to do here. It appears that wasn't quite true. It's been written in the stars all along, and it took me most of my life to understand and confess to it! I am seriously slow!"

"I'd call those cosmic credentials, Aunt Joni. As I've said before, I didn't think you could outdo anything you've already shared. But that does it. My mind will never be the same, and that, too, is official!"

"Thank you. Congratulations and condolences!" Aunt Joni offered with a big smile.

"And with that, I'm realizing I've seriously sidetracked us, haven't I?"

"You're tracking, all right!" Aunt Joni teased me, obviously delighted to have made an impact on my consciousness yet again.

I raised my glass into the air and tilted it toward her to toast the moment and acknowledge our work in progress.

"So, back to Helen Palmer. She taught me that being a child of two alcoholic parents can be an extraordinary gift – if you can survive it! That statement of hers hit me hard. I had to look with fresh eyes at the horror of those years growing up with Eloise and Bill. Half of those adult children of alcoholics – perhaps more – do not escape the behavioral patterns and follow a well-worn path into alcoholism themselves. Helen Palmer observed over the course of decades working with children of alcoholics that often they have already developed intuitive pathways – whether they realize it or not."

"Those are some mind-boggling bad odds, Aunt Joni. I think about all the members of our family over time, all the way to the present, who've drunk their way through life. Our family odds might be even worse than fifty-fifty. I'd venture to guess we have far more family who've been victims of the alcohol battle than the military variety. But I still don't get it. How does alcoholism somehow develop intuition in the children of alcoholics?"

"One of Helen Palmer's students asked the same question. She responded that it was vital for us to know before we walked through the door whether our inebriated parents were passed out or prepared to knock us around or otherwise abuse us. We relied on every available sense we had to survive."

"That makes a whole lot more sense to me when you put it into context."

"It is plain to see that much of the world is descended from generations of alcoholism."

"That explains an awful lot!"

"Take those entrenched alcoholic routines a step farther and think about all the other forms of addiction out there capturing our attention – for how long is anyone's guess, I suppose. It all starts with the fixation of the attention on habit."

"I see what you mean. I've developed habits without even thinking about it!"

"Do you remember me sharing long ago that worrying is like praying for what you don't want?"

"Yes, I haven't forgotten that gem. It's stopped me on many an occasion from continuing to worry as I've become more conscious of my own mental patterns."

"Our producer, Robert, added a tagline I'd never heard, courtesy of his wonderful wife, Kitta."

"Oh? What's that?"

"That worry is a debt that can never be repaid."

"That is also powerful! It speaks to the residual damage from the stress we create for ourselves. Wow! All of this gives me a whole new level of understanding about the mental health issues in this country – not to mention our own family. It never occurred to me how historically deep-seated alcoholism and other mental illnesses might really be."

"So, back to Helen Palmer. She cautioned her students that intuitive senses are gifts to us and must be used appropriately – never for harm, intrusion, or personal gain. The consequences of misuse could be immediate and devastating. As I began to grasp some of this, I half-jokingly referred to it as 'instant karmic ketchup.' The consequences of any ill-advised action would come back at me in a hurry, leaving me with a mess to clean up!" She smiled and shook her head.

"That's a classic, Aunt Joni!" I immediately had an image of myself sitting at the dinner table, watching my instant-karmic ketchup splatter off my french fries and cover me, the table, and the floor with a mess. I had to laugh out loud. It wasn't a humorous subject, but the analogy hit home instantly. "I've certainly had to clean up more than a few of my own messes in life. But I'm still not clear about all of this. So, how would I know that I've actually had an intuitive experience?"

"You've arrived at the heart of the matter, nephew. Helen Palmer addressed your question directly. She shared that there was a way to know whether or not it was the real deal!"

"Seriously? How can you tell?"

"She taught us to assess whether an intuitive occurrence was a product of consciousness or from beyond consciousness by identifying where our attention was focused at the time the intuitive information came through to us. Was the attention focused on thought in consciousness, or was it following the breath in and out of the lower diaphragm?"

My aunt paused to take a drink. I hadn't moved a muscle. She was now getting down to some serious details. As I tried to digest her last explanation, I felt my brain freeze up. It was so much for me to take in, and I knew I was still missing something. "Okay, I think you may have covered this with me at some point in the past, but I'm needing a basic refresher. When you refer to my 'attention,' what are you really talking about? What is my attention?"

"Your attention *is* whatever it is focused upon or captured by," she replied, pausing just long enough to allow me to consider her words. "Your attention will spin around indefinitely in consciousness throughout life as a matter of habit. Or, with direction and training, you can train your attention to follow the breath in and out of the lower diaphragm, no longer in consciousness as we know it."

"Okay! That was a critical question, all right. I'm getting it. Thank you for that review."

"Helen Palmer referred to our attention as our eternal observer. That was a huge missing link for me as well," she added quietly.

"That's powerful! And what a different perspective on reality to hold my attention in that frame of reference!"

"Buddha called it our 'true law nature,' which I mentioned earlier."

"No kidding? That's mind-blowing! Will you say more about that now? Is he saying what I think he's saying?"

"What he's saying is that the space where both conscious mind and physical body are still is the true nature of our existence."

"Wow! That is huge!" I cried as I began to get my head around this extraordinary revelation.

"In that place, that space, and in those moments, we are all connected," she added. "The problem is that as soon as we try to put our true law nature into words, we've blown it and superficially limited that which is infinite."

"I see the issue. It's the semantics that get in the way, isn't it?"

"Just because we don't use a common vocabulary to communicate with one another about infinity, doesn't negate it or its complexities. One only needs to see deep space once in a while to be reminded of a work of art millions and millions of light-years in the making."

"Isn't that the truth? The view of the night sky from here is out of this world! I keep coming back to one of your most helpful hints from years ago: that we're each our own self-limiting factors, Aunt Joni. That really helped me." It dawned on me at that moment that consciousness really was a self-absorbing perspective. When I turned off my brain, my senses expanded to be with the stars, leaving me in an extraordinary state of calm.

"Eternity is out there and inside of us," she replied quietly. "Sure, it's simpler to keep our heads in the sand, ignore our universal connections, and play childishly in our own little box with a view, with our feelings of self-importance – our egos – leading us to destroy one another's sandcastles. Palmer taught that we really only need to maintain enough ego to survive – the rest inevitably gets in the way."

"Wow, that's a bit to get my head around," I replied.

"Carl Gustav Jung was another mentor, a truly great scientist," she added. "He proved the mind has the capability to exist beyond the constraints of space and time."

"Seriously? What does that even mean?"

"It means we have the ability to extend, or replicate, if you will, our psyche to other locations than the one in which our physical body is residing."

"Whoa! For real, huh? Has anyone else written about that?"

"Paramahansa Yogananda wrote about it in *Autobiography of a Yogi*. Carlos Castaneda wrote about it in his many books. Buddha discusses it in his sutras from the experience of an array of his lifetimes. It is one of the many spiritual capacities that human beings can develop, resulting from meditation and expanding wisdom."

"Have you experienced this, Aunt Joni?"

"Yes, I have. The most significant occurrence for me was being with your grandma Eloise after she passed. When my conscious mind got an inkling of what was happening with a view of deep space surrounding her during that visit, I was freaked enough that it brought me back immediately with an enormous inhale of apprehension."

"Un-fucking-believable! Are you going to share more about that in volume three?"

"Yes, dear. I will. And I don't want to lose my train of thought about Carl Jung. The man deserves accolades for his volumes in psychology after having studied people the world around during his lifetime. If we were all able to understand his contributions, I am of the belief we'd certainly be in a different place."

"That's all pretty extraordinary, Aunt Joni. I had no idea! What were his ideas?" I asked, floored by all of these latest revelations.

"Great teachers like Helen Palmer and C.G. Jung are not that common. Some of Jung's efforts have made their way into popular culture – for example, awareness of intuition and the collective unconscious are both more broadly understood as universal human experiences today due to his work. Much of it, however, has been buried in the ever-increasing overload of information we're deluged with every day."

"I can relate to that. I can't seem to keep up with anything!" I responded fervently.

"Jung's insights for humanity are profound. Summaries of his work provide an overview of the breadth of his efforts and the depths of the human psyche. Penguin Books published the *Portable Jung* decades ago, and it's still worth the read. When you're ready, after an introduction that can provide you context for what he's talking about, I'd nominate his autobiography, *Memories, Dreams & Reflections*, written at the tail end of his life, as a must-read for your own proverbial bucket list."

"Thanks, Aunt Joni. Will you say more?"

"His collected scientific volumes are said to be able to fill a room. It's not well known anymore that he mentored under Freud and had to start by debunking Freud's work. Jung was exacting in his discipline, processes, and findings. None of his personal experiences would ever be included in these volumes. Everything he was able to prove, he did across numerous patients, cultures, and countries throughout the world. At the end of his life, at the urging of his students, he was finally able to review his scientific effort and include his own personal and spiritual experiences, providing the backdrop for the rest of us to understand how he was able to make such extraordinary leaps in understanding for humanity."

"Okay, I get it. The man had to be a genius! Thanks for the suggestion, Aunt Joni. I'll put it on the proverbial list! I wasn't that familiar with his work."

"Most of us missed his point and his greater efforts entirely or didn't know what to do with them. In hindsight, his work might have been treated as some of the great scientific discoveries of the century for humanity. But no such luck yet. Our blinders are many."

"You can say that again," I agreed, shaking my head. "But why do you suppose we are so blind to this stuff? Is it really all about some form of transcendental phobia, or what?"

"There were other historical factors that have played a huge role in the Western world's seeming blindness to all things spiritual. It's one of the topics of volume two, if you can be patient. However, I'll note for now there was a long period in Western spiritual history where humans had the opposite problem relative to that deluge of information we experience now."

"Oh?"

"Those who purportedly had spiritual wisdom would rationalize passing it from one elite religious group to another in the name of protecting and preserving 'their' wisdom from harm. That went on for a very long time in many places. Even the Bible went through its own history of being largely unavailable to the public, or under wraps, if you will – clerical wraps!"

I laughed at her imagery. "You have a knack for taking on seriously huge subjects and somehow finding humor in the process. I'm learning it is seriously helpful to have a sense of humor along the proverbial way!"

My aunt nodded in agreement. "Helen Palmer maintained that in modern times, all of the keys to the great wisdom are known. They are all out there to be rediscovered. The greater challenge is separating the wheat from the chaff – and passing it on in a manner that's understandable."

I gave her a quizzical look.

"The irony is that people often believe that anything offered free of charge, or offered freely by someone, can't, by definition, be worth much. Why else would someone give it away? We are raised to believe that most everything is purportedly worth something – even our lives are assigned a monetary value."

"Wow, I never thought about it that way," I said sheepishly.

"We train ourselves, with quite a bit of help, to want and value those material rewards. However, if I might be so bold." She paused.

"What is it, Joni? What were you going to say?"

"When you do the math and begin to factor in the multipliers over time, these *Torch Time Tales* were not free. They came at an astronomically high price to our family and to countless people our family members ultimately impacted along the way. We must herewith offer an apology to each one, along with a genuine effort at amends. I know that with one 'whit-more' sense, all our relations might have the cross-generational clarity to pick up the pieces and learn from one another and about one another through time and space."

I was stunned by her statements. "Is there something specific you have in mind?"

"Yes! It is the second spiritual apology to humanity from our family of ancestors in the last five hundred years. Would you like to hear it?"

"You're not kidding, are you?" I sighed. "Remind me to ask you about the first apology, or is that for volume two?" I asked, though I knew the answer. "Yes, Aunt Joni, I absolutely want to hear this. Please proceed."

"Think this through. With ignorance relegated to history and each of us self-realized within our true law nature, we will share an infinite mind in a state of equality. To get there, we need to look back before we look forward – to recognize our sins, ego-driven mistakes, and crimes against humanity, not only in our lives but in the lifetimes of our ancestors. Our individual, familial, and institutional mistakes have caused harm and suffering through the generations. We can recognize, apologize, do penance, and practice justice accordingly."

"I'll second that," I responded.

"I pray with all of my being that these efforts will make that just-noticeable difference toward healing everyone's mind, spirit, and body. So, here is what I have learned, here is what I recognize, and herewith is my apology."

CHAPTER 22

An Apology for True Universal Divinity

I turn once again to you, my patient audience. You'll recall, dear friends and family, that Aunt Joni had just given me a heads up that she was about to share with me big time. I'll note her "apology" parallels one that was written hundreds of years ago by one of Grandma Winn's ancestors. That's in volume two!

Little did I realize the extraordinary parallels she'd discovered. I do know Aunt Joni continues to set nearly impossible goals and then work her butt off to achieve them, or as she'd say, at least make a dent. With that said, I give you Aunt Joni.

* * *

Equality under the true law, found within our true law nature, is deterred only by ignorance. The rest is about discriminations of the conscious mind resulting from learned behavior. Ignorance was identified by Sakyamuni Buddha as the first principle of the twelvefold causal-link chain of human suffering more than twenty-five hundred years ago.

When seven-plus billion people have recognized it is possible that we are all connected, the true law shall begin to be realized again. The remaining learned discriminations of our conscious ego minds can begin to melt away like morning dew, Buddha added.

May God grant me the clarity to understand that my ego-driven, self-righteous learned behavior slows my journey to tread the path less traveled to the universal self-realization that we share an infinite mind.

I'll continue the process outlined by true universal laws, including confessing my sins and those of my genealogical ancestors for ALL of it: including the sins of my eyes, ears, nose, mouth, body, and, our greatest sense organ, my mind. With thanks forever to all those whose patient, gentle, tactful energy here, now, above, and beyond helps us move along the great river's way.

Perhaps this might contribute to that just noticeable difference toward movement for all. Of course, the problems are bigger than all of us individually, right? Shouldn't we each get off the hook?

Let it begin with me, then. I will assume the cloak of shame for my own humanity and humbly offer my personal and my family's deepest apologies toward one and all in a start to a truly comprehensive reparations process.

For all the suffering, slavery, subordination, incarceration, oppression, discrimination, decimation, genocide, pain, grief, anger, illness, and death my ancestors and I have brought to others of all forms through and from time immemorial to the present, I offer my humble and heartfelt apology to all toward a universal, comprehensive reparations process.

Our inability to realize our responsibilities to one another, which are infinite in scope, continues to delay the movement of the collective assemblage point of our global attention to where it could be for all. I am therefore reformulating my living and estate plans to create ongoing vehicles for change. Profits will be dedicated toward the elimination of ignorance and poverty.

CHAPTER 23

Watch Out for Hammers!

"Wow! Where'd that come from?" I asked Aunt Joni after she'd finished her apology.

"I'm continuing the process outlined by true universal laws, including confessing my sins and those of my ancestors."

"Aunt Joni, you continue to blow my crazy mind. Are you nuts or what? You are totally serious about all of this, aren't you?"

"Thankfully, you don't have to take my word for any of it. The truth and the infinite universe are all inside and out there for you to discover in real time, in your own time."

"The craziest part about all of this? I think I understand you!" I replied, laughing.

My aunt took my comment in stride. "Ongoing vehicles for education, enlightenment, and ultimately, sustainable change are essential. That's part of my intent with the perpetual literary trust, for it to serve as a vehicle for restitution, reconciliatory justice, recompense, and atonement."

"Oh, my God, you are serious! I think I'm finally getting the family picture! And I think my mind as I used to know it will never be the same!" I added with a big smile on my face.

"Expand the circle wider, and one might view America as our dysfunctional national family. Its history is interwoven and parallels our own, as you'll see throughout the volumes of *Torch Time Tales*."

"I totally see how our family history, with its ups and downs, successes and scandals, mirrors the US history of the same periods. But I never in my wildest imagination would have believed any of it!" I added with amazement.

"Damage done to the people of this planet over the course of human history is incalculable, but it doesn't have to remain unaddressed. We can develop the clarity to live together respectfully as unique individuals and cultures when we recognize that despite all of our differences, we share equality within our true law nature, with universal intelligence. God knows there are blinders and obstacles to overcome for us to get there as a family, much less a nation or a planet."

"I totally get it!" I added enthusiastically.

"We share one outrageous family history! It's impossible to imagine it all, much less relate to it, until the history is truly your own. Learning about history in a book distances us from the actual historical events – they have no real context for us. But when it becomes clear the history is ours to own, we can see how it impacts us personally," she observed, picking up her glass of water.

"You are going to get no more arguments from me on that one, Aunt Joni. It gives a whole new meaning for me to 'own something,' as I own my family's history instead of just a material possession. I'm now convinced our family history is outrageous, to say the least, and I'm now owning more of it than I ever dreamed possible. These are truly experiences of a lifetime for me. How can I thank you?"

"How can I thank you, your brother, your father, and your cousin Paula for all your help? You will have countless opportunities over the course of your lifetime to share and give back to others what you've learned in life. I'm counting on it!" She chuckled.

"Okay, okay, so what else have you got to say for yourself?" I tossed back to her.

"The greatest heights and lowest depths of humanity are closer than we ever realized – and have literally shaped us, our relations, and our extended national and global families. Each individual, busy with daily living, misses the significance of understanding our personal ancestral evolution and trauma and what that history has done to our own understanding of ourselves and others through time."

"That hits home for me with our family history," I responded, nodding. I'd had no idea how my family history had helped shape who I was until I'd learned more about it – eventually, it all clicked into place.

"We can thank all of the great teachers over time for helping us to see there is more to life than the limits of our conscious reality – and for all contributions, great and small, that help expand our ability to see clearly and grow together toward self-respecting pillars for humanity. Slowly, slowly, more of the technological pieces are coming together, enabling communication across disciplines to make that more probable. The potential for self-realization globally is within sight for your generation. You've chosen an exciting time to be alive, truly!"

"Do you really think so?" I responded, still skeptical at that point that human nature could pull its collective head out of its behind.

"I think you have the potential to thrive like never before!" Joni said, getting excited all over again. "Every era brings tools and understanding not previously accessible or widely shared around the globe." I watched her fidget a moment as she collected her thoughts.

"So, if I'm following, we will open up the degrees of possibilities, literally the range of capacities and opportunities for everyone, when we're able to recognize and release ourselves from our own self-limiting factors!"

"Yes! I'll take it a step farther," she added. "It's brash to say, but if we are able to respectfully set aside our religious differences, even for one moment, to appreciate Jung's findings that the mind can exist beyond the constraints of space and time, it's possible we might then willfully choose to prioritize understanding the importance of our attention, our Eternal Observer, throughout our respective cultures, with everyone strengthened along the way. The growing strength of the personal, familial, and societal peace of mind and clarity should take care of the rest of it."

"What a concept! And I get it!" I responded happily.

"I've had my hands full trying to understand the lessons I've been served in my own lifetime – they've unfolded faster than I could integrate them. When I first began experiencing intuition directly, I didn't know what to make of it. Eventually, I called these experiences universal hammers."

"Why did you call them that?" I asked quietly.

"They were direct and powerful, and they kept happening. I couldn't ignore them. It felt to me in hindsight that the universe had to use a hammer to get through my thick skull and get me to pay attention!" she said, laughing at herself. "I have many to thank for guiding me along the way, for without them, I may not have survived! And thank you, dear one. You've made my journey complete."

"I'm the one that should be thanking you. Thanks for having me!" I replied sheepishly.

Aunt Joni, now well beyond her mature years, just as foretold in the stars, let out a long sigh. "You are most welcome!"

CHAPTER 24

Questions Repeated That I Couldn't Ignore

"You've worked with people on so many different levels over your life, Aunt Joni. Were there any requests that repeated themselves over time that really get to the heart of all of this?"

"There are definitely times in our lives, often unexpected and unavoidable, in which we are called to service on behalf of another. What's critical about this is that service or 'help' may or may not be the right thing to do, above and beyond whether or to what extent we might be able to help at all. With each request, we face a potentially difficult decision in life – do we assist or not? And perhaps more importantly, by purportedly helping, will we do more harm than good?"

"I never thought about it quite like that. Will you say more?"

"Clearly, enabling someone to continue some of the worst of their poorly chosen habits is not helping them. Yet intervention, when unwanted, generally backfires. So, we may be compelled to set boundaries around what we can and do give in the precious space and time we share with another."

"I'm imagining you're describing rescuing someone from a serious quagmire."

"Many have written about this subject. One perspective is that to truly help someone, you can't give a damn about them. You also can't give a damn whether someone is going to like you, dislike you, or ignore you."

"Huh?" I replied. "I don't get that."

"If we give a damn, it may be because we want something in return for helping. To truly help, one cannot want anything in return. As Helen Palmer imparted, true wisdom is priceless. Anything less has a price tag of one form or another. It boils down to more of that attachment business – in this case, attachment to wanting something in return."

"Okay, okay. I'm getting it," I responded

"One must also have an idea of the personal baggage we might bring to the table that would interfere with truly helping someone," my aunt continued.

"Our personal baggage," I repeated, now understanding the meaning of what she was trying to convey. I flashed to my ex-girlfriend from years ago and the emotional mess I'd been in when I'd arrived at my aunt's. Somewhere along the way, I'd forgotten all about it. It had been a process, however, to get there, to progress to the point where I was able to let go of the emotional baggage I'd created.

"In my life, I had periods when settling down to sleep was the time my mind raised all those 'things' in life that were unsettled, that I had not resolved. It was my 'busy' mind, attempting to clear through my own personal trunk of leftover stuff – my own emotional baggage."

"I can relate to that. Exams used to keep me up at night while I was in school; now, periodically, it's something that's happened at work or something my boss might have said to me."

"I realized it was a developmental stage, a process that must be an integral part of life – the part where I took stock. Clearly, I would have been sunk by the load of my baggage had I not processed some of it along the way. No, this was to process the deluge of things that happened faster than I could process at the time. If it doesn't get resolved by the mind, we carry it around until it does – like baggage! Baggage is part of the stuff of life, what 'matters' in life, what life is about, this process of integrating our life experience with reality as we understand it in all forms."

"So, in other words, if you're carrying too much personal baggage, you're less likely to be able to truly relieve someone else of their own load?"

"You get the drift. Take, for example, parenting, a process I now view in hindsight as a school within a school. I'm beginning to see that it is as much for the human development of the parent as for the child. We want so much for our children – the deeply felt need to see them go farther, reach higher, experience or have what we didn't in life. At some point, we expect them, as if by osmosis, to know everything we've already learned, and we are disappointed or angry when they make the same mistakes."

"That hits home, and I don't even have any children yet!" I responded, thinking of my parents.

"Inescapably, we raise our children in a manner that inadvertently imparts both what we wanted and didn't want to give them. And as they age, they provide powerful reflections as to who we were growing up and who we are now – in a way we couldn't understand, see, or appreciate earlier in our lives. Youth is self-absorbed. Maturity can be a self-pity party. It is all about us at both points in our development. And youths and elders alike can act and behave as if we know it all. We are often more alike than we are different."

"So, children become mirrors for adults," I repeated, which served as a cue to my aunt that I had gotten the message.

"Politics provides another example – the penultimate reflection of who we are and where we are in our societal development. Politicians are charged with having an answer, or at least an opinion, on the spot for everything, every question. Not knowing is perceived as weakness, ill-preparedness. And ironically, the more they act like they know everything, the less we like them. When they clearly don't know it all and things go wrong, we want to throw them out and start over, only to start the same process all over again."

"I can certainly think of more than a few presidents that fit that description," I replied.

"Politics is the curious cyclical vetting process we use to attempt to find leaders – people who can lead us forward out of the mess that is our collective state of mind. And the process of our political system provides powerful ongoing insulating cover for the plain fact that we are, each and every one of us, responsible parties – while our 'representative' gives us someone else to blame!"

"I'm hearing the responsibility theme again, Aunt Joni. I have to tell you, after all of this, I feel a hell of a lot more responsible than I ever did before!"

"That's terrific to hear! It's absurd that a nation founded on personal liberties denied fundamental human rights to all for so long. Yet the ignorance of the day is the norm and has been the norm for a long, long time. People owned, controlled, and often killed others to take what they wanted over the course of human history. Those patterns of behavior were long entrenched before they reached the shores of what would become America. Her own manifest destiny, as it was grandly called in the day, was ultimately, to me, a metaphor for plowing over the backs of peoples already there as she bulldozed her way west, wiping out or disturbing most along the way."

"I have to say, Aunt Joni, when I contrast the reality of what actually happened in Western history with the smattering of misinformation that I was taught, I am just totally flabbergasted."

"Well, perhaps, as a place to start, we might agree that our respective familial experience and educational base have shaped each of our personal, emotional, spiritual, and hence, political vantage points. It seems appropriate for all of us to acknowledge that our respective and collective points of view are often going to point us in divergent directions."

"That's a powerful statement. It makes a lot more sense to me now."

"We all have different sets of life experiences and knowledge. Freedom of speech, in combination with our egos, when left unchecked, virtually demands that we be heard – only to face a range of potential responses, from agreement to arrest to ridicule or argument from others. It is certainly easier to talk to ourselves or to those we know share our point of view. It can be awfully uncomfortable to do otherwise, and it's understandable why many people stop trying."

"I'll second that," I added, remembering all the arguments I'd been in about politics – absurd arguments at that.

"It all becomes a very complicated spiral, indeed. How do we all move forward? Again, our respective starting points aim us toward different understandings of what is ideal. So often in politics, this personalized ideal is intertwined with religious ideas that some insist everyone else follow. Numerous faiths assert theirs to be the way, the only right path – all others doomed to fail by definition of a form alien to us."

"It's all so complicated, but you seem to be able to tease it out in a way that is really helping me to get clear about what's going on, Aunt Joni."

"I'm so very happy to hear it. As Helen Palmer observed, it is known there are 360 degrees to a circle. What each respective point irrevocably has in common with every other degree is the center. All around the world, we have our differences, but at the center, like with the circle, we are all one. It doesn't matter what you call our true universal divinity. Our words cannot destroy the *all that is*. The fight about it has been for real, don't get me wrong, and it has been life-and-death stuff for a long time. Don't be fooled."

"Okay, okay, stop a minute. There's another powerful analogy you just threw out there that I want to get my head around before you get going again. So, if I understand you, what you're getting at is that we're fighting one another to defend our learned behavior and values in life while missing the universal truth of the connection among us that ought to be able to put any disagreement into a more relative, compassionate perspective."

"That's a different speed on that spin, and yes, you're getting it," she replied excitedly. "The adage that we cannot forget the past lest we be doomed to repeat it in the future has elements of truth. Yet if it were truly as simple as that, wouldn't we have figured out a new way forward by now? Aren't we continuing to make the same mistakes?"

"It sure seems like it to me," I replied.

"The inverse adage as applied to the financial world, and cast in concrete as a standard regulatory warning, is that past performance is no indication of future results. These are perhaps two sides of the same coin, and yet again, it comes back to our perspective. Is our glass half full, half empty, or, as your cousin's father used to say, twice as large as it needs to be?"

"Okay, okay, you've made your point!"

"Helen Palmer relayed that when we can step off the path expected of us, or that we expect of ourselves, we open up the realm of possibility in our lives by 360 degrees. And she granted and cautioned that statistics suggest that at least 180 of those degrees – some of those possibilities, in other words – might have negative implications. Yet with that step also means a far greater radius of potentiality and outcomes."

"That goes without saying for me. I'll never be the same again!" At that point, we broke out in laughter. It was all we could do. It was now beyond obvious to me that it was a true statement.

"So, I come back full circle to the question of helping one another: where do we go from here?" Aunt Joni finally asked herself rhetorically. "I'm struck by a myriad of examples that suggest that one of the keys to a positive outcome lies in the quality, timing, and accessibility of the information available to each individual. The tricky part is that our ability to receive it, process it, and integrate it depends on our base of understanding. Too much too soon, and it is meaningless to us, over our heads. Too little too late, and we are bored with the routine, frustrated by the inanity. Too many of our long-cherished filters shading our eyes, and we'll miss our hands in front of our face."

"This is ringing a bell for something you mentioned earlier," I interjected, but there was no stopping her in the moment. My aunt was once again on a roll.

"It appears ignorance is still the easiest place to live," she commented, "yet potentially far more dangerous to us than that which we fear. Perhaps we just fear the unknown."

"I think you might be onto something, Aunt Joni," I added, my left eyebrow raised.

"As I was ruminating about this one afternoon, an old friend offered that it sounded like I was trying to describe a transcendental phobia. I can tell you I searched for a word that would fit that definition shortly thereafter, and ironically, I found no such word."

"What are you getting at?"

"I think you could describe it as a struggle that plays out within consciousness. Awareness of celestial matters awakens consciousness to the limitations of ego. That awareness might initially be frightening or may provoke anxiety on an existential level for the conscious mind."

"I'm getting it. Especially if one has no spiritual context to explain what they've experienced!"

"That's vital. As we've seen with our family, change in our lifetime can be difficult enough to handle on many levels. Many will avoid it at all costs. The practical reality that we can transcend our thought process, our behavior, or even our physical bodies seems out of reach, out of the realm of possibility for many in today's world. Who has that kind of time? And what doors might we open to discover consequences we'd just as soon not face? Over our lifetimes, perhaps we ought to be more afraid of our capacity to do damage to one another." She shook her head.

"Yeah, we've normalized a lot of really ugly behavior over time, haven't we?"

"You've gotten to the heart of it again, my dear nephew. The insidious part *is* the process of rationalizing one's behavior. When we are unable to get our minds completely around something to understand it, we rationalize and essentially reduce whatever it is to the elements we think we do understand or that our psyche can handle understanding. In the process, our conscious mind then allows us off the hook for our personal behavior and involvement."

"I never thought about it that way, but I see what you mean. I've seen a lot of folks rationalize really bad stuff over the course of my life."

"The process of rationalization further contributes to our being afraid of things we don't understand. I was aghast to learn from a 2011 study by the Pew Charitable Trust that Americans appeared to be equally as frightened of Buddhism as they were of Islam. Any amount of effort to understand Buddhism as a compassionate philosophy of life ought to quickly wash away any fear."

"That's just incredible to me. How could people reach such crazy conclusions?"

"They arrive at that place out of ignorance, dear one. A simple lack of awareness may lead us to presumptions and assumptions that can unknowingly get us into all kinds of trouble!"

"I hadn't really thought about presumptions and assumptions being essentially the same thing. One just precedes the other, I guess."

"Take them many, many steps further and understand that the world is full of sovereigns and religious institutions who've been literally enshrined in their positions as the ultimate authority of their respective flavor of rationalization and have continued rationalizing their uninterrupted power-over abuses since time immemorial."

"Oh, good heavens, Aunt Joni. Now you appear to be getting to the heart of it. I get it."

"Life and the languages of lifetimes evolve and digress in tandem, my dear nephew. How many times in life have you heard the expression 'pay attention'?"

"Boatloads, for sure! However, I have to point out you're the first one to ever define for me what that really means! Thanks, Aunt Joni!"

"Helen Palmer encouraged us to look at our attention as a muscle that can be strengthened over time. I've found that to be a really helpful perspective."

"I see what you mean. All these years later, it's made a difference in my life."

"So, where is the focus of our societal attention now?"

I didn't respond. It was her cue that she could continue, that I was following.

"Often it is captured by violence, blame, shame, and the need to pass the buck. We herd one another using fear, greed, anger, and self-righteousness, often for the power or the personal satisfaction that exudes when we perceive ourselves to be right, to have the answer." She stretched. "It's time to get control of your mind before someone else does!"

"That's powerful! You can say that again! It's hard to look at the news and not be outraged."

"What repeats itself throughout the ages is truth, assuming we can still identify it as such. And we have many to thank for their efforts and attempts, made at great personal expense, to bring truth to light."

"It appears to be far more precious than I might have realized! I think about all the bullshit that's been frontloaded into my brain that's useless! All that time wasted," I lamented.

"You've brought me to an inescapable point, dear nephew. Thank you!"

I looked at her quizzically, having no idea what she would say next.

"Every last thing that's been frontloaded into your brain, as you say – your conscious mind, I would say – is learned behavior."

As the fates would have it, as if to help Aunt Joni cement these memories within me, a hummingbird flew to the window to check on us. It hovered in place, obviously curious as to what we were doing inside. We broke out into laughter.

"Playing with hummingbirds can also be learned behavior!" my aunt observed with a happy smile as she pushed back the sliding glass door so we could head outside.

"We have a lot to be thankful for, don't we, Aunt Joni?"

"Yes, indeed. I've worked diligently in my life to give back and pay forward to others the kindness and compassion shared with me, and I'm not satisfied that I've repaid my debts of gratitude. It's kept me going. I've attempted, when possible, to assist those directed to me for a whole host of reasons under the sun – and some, I've refused, setting healthy limits for myself in the process when it wasn't necessarily the right thing to do. Sometimes I was successful in the moment; other times, not so much!"

"So, were there any requests, in particular, that stand out for you?" I was curious how she might respond.

"As I sit with where we are now, a couple of requests come to mind. Why don't we regroup with some refreshments and make a fresh start of it here in a bit?"

How could I disagree?

★ ★ ★

"Decades ago, in Homer, Alaska, an elderly man with a long white beard and cane showed up one early evening at the Old

Inlet Trading Post, asking to see me. After one of the resident artists had clued me in that there was someone who wanted to talk to me, I set aside my work and made my way to the front of the gallery. We had never met before. I introduced myself to the man, who shook my hand and replied that his name was John Ireland."

"That's a little odd, don't you think?" I queried her, wondering how I'd react if someone fitting the description of Old Saint Nick showed up at my door unannounced, wanting to see me.

"Mr. Ireland explained he'd been referred by mutual friends of ours – they were a pair of amazingly wonderful sisters, Andrea and Nan, who were healers. They had been trained in therapeutic massage and then developed their art form to a spiritual level of service to others. And in the spirit of true gifts to humanity, the pair worked for nothing. At some point, their paths had crossed with John's. He'd shared his particular plight with them, and although they weren't able to help him, he told me they knew who would."

"So that explains how it came to pass that John Ireland came to see you…but what about his plight? What was his problem?" I pressed, wanting to know for myself.

"Before I continue, I have to tell you that as fate would have it, the women were killed, along with Andrea's daughter, not long after that in a tragic accident on the Alaska-Canadian Highway. Their passing was an enormous loss for the community. So many people were moved by their genuinely wonderful spirits and all their efforts on behalf of others."

"Wow, Aunt Joni," I stammered, shocked by that twist in fate. "And John Ireland?"

"John appeared to me at first blush to be quite anxious about something. The look on his face when he introduced himself suggested he was, perhaps, skeptical that the much younger woman standing in front of him that he'd been referred to was going to be able to help him."

"What did he want from you?" I asked her, now even more intrigued.

"He wanted to find peace of mind. He was near the end of his life – and time was running out for him to figure it out. He had spent years walking hundreds of miles in Alaska, trying to find it, but to no avail. It hadn't helped him. All he felt was anxiety and a foreboding sense of urgency. He had spent his entire life that way, unable to find peace. By that point, he knew he needed and wanted help."

I looked at my aunt quizzically. "Do people just show up at your door every day with existential questions for you, or what?"

"Or at the fence." My aunt laughed and gestured toward the pond. "That's a story for volume three. Anyway, when I asked John if he meditated, he looked befuddled and asked me what I meant. And when I began to describe a simple Buddhist emptying practice, as it's typically called, of stilling the busyness of consciousness, I watched as disbelief and then realization washed over his face."

"Why so? What am I missing here?" I interjected, really wanting to understand his reaction.

"And then out came the crux of it that I'd missed along the way in my attempts to understand him in those moments. John had learned from religious instruction as a young person that if he ever allowed his mind to be still, even for a moment, it would surely make room for the devil."

"You're not kidding! Really?" When the full realization of his dilemma hit me, I confess I was floored. I could easily see how the consequences of such a destructive thought process planted in the mind of an impressionable person would drive the strongest of us up a mountain and beyond to pursue an ever-elusive peace of mind. "Oh, my God!" I finally exclaimed.

"He had spent every waking day since trying to make sure that didn't happen and was near to driving himself insane," Joni added, interrupting my own train of thought on the matter. "In his case, John had continued to do the same thing over and over again as his mind continued to endlessly spin, yet he somehow expected to get a different result!"

I had to agree with her that this was insane, and I knew the story had left a deep impression on me. It's fair to say I never forgot it for a whole host of reasons. When I've lost it, I know for myself that I can't live without it anymore. Peace of mind is the place to be.

* * *

We'd taken another break to stretch our bodies as John Ireland's tale continued to resonate between us. It was hard not to imagine him continuously forcing his mind to keep moving for fear of what stopping the whirl might uncover. All these years later in my life, I'm so thankful to know stilling consciousness brings soothing relief. It has more than a fleeting impact on the mind and body.

"So, Aunt Joni, am I remembering there was another tale like the last one that you wanted to share?"

"Thanks for the reminder!" She smiled. "Another fifteen years went by before I had another request quite like that last one. Upon return to a local tailor in Bangkok for a fitting, I found the middle-aged proprietor very upset. The day before, he had begged my husband, John, who had been in the mental health field, to review the medications prescribed for his anxiety. John had to repeatedly refuse him before he let the matter drop."

"That's a little strange."

"The next day, I returned alone. I soon learned the man had not slept through the night for over a decade. He had a wife and first family he maintained in Pakistan, but things had gotten increasingly dangerous there."

"When was this?" I asked, attempting to put the conversation into context.

"Oh, I'd have to check my logs to be sure; somewhere around 2006, 2007, I'm guessing. So, without telling anyone for fear others in Pakistan might target him, he flew by himself to Thailand and set up shop on the island of Phuket."

"It sounds like he had reason to be afraid."

"The man took on a second wife and began a second family there on the island. So, fast forward. They managed to survive the Great Tsunami of 2004, but their business near the beach was totally destroyed. As they began to try to recover and rebuild, the tragedy continued to haunt them. I remember him explaining to me that they couldn't get the ghastly images left over from that horrific event out of their minds."

"Wow, this is unbelievably sad."

"So, finally, he made the decision to move his second family to Bangkok and open a new shop near the river to provide them a fresh start. But the stress of supporting two families in two countries became overwhelming for him."

"I can't even begin to imagine. I know, most days, I wonder about my ability to manage myself!" We chuckled at the truth of that statement. "So, then what happened? What did he say?"

"So, as with John Ireland, the tailor was pretty quickly able to get to the crux of his issue. 'What is the meaning of life?' he asked me anxiously, clearly under great duress. I could see him sweating the stress. 'What is the meaning of life?' he asked again, louder this time. 'What is the meaning of life?' he cried a third and final time.

My aunt paused before continuing. "There was no one else there but me to hear him. The man was clearly in crisis. Three excruciatingly painful times, he had pleaded for understanding. The timing of this moment happened for a reason, although I don't understand it. When I quietly offered that I couldn't answer that question for him but that there might be a method that would allow him both peace of mind and restful nights without the medication, he quickly took a seat to listen."

"Humph," was all I could manage, once again well caught up in the tale.

"At that point, I had his undivided attention. The man had tied his knot and was hanging on. When I asked him if he meditated, he replied he didn't know what that meant. 'You mean to tell me you live in a city that is ninety percent Buddhist and you've never heard of meditation?' I asked him incredulously, speaking without thinking. 'I'm a Pakistani Muslim,' he responded indignantly, rightly offended by my flippant response."

"Oh, dear, Aunt Joni, what happened?"

"I realized I had unintentionally insulted him is what happened," my aunt replied before continuing. "Okay, I said to him, 'I am so sorry. I apologize. It was not my intent to insult you. Can we agree to set religion aside for a moment and just focus on the practice?'"

"How did he respond?"

"Thankfully, he agreed. And when I finished describing and diagramming for him and was sure he'd gotten it, I said that it had been recommended to me that one practice for ten minutes at a time, once in the morning and once in the evening, every day so, rather than being a burden, it might instead become a lifetime companion." My aunt paused a moment to sip her beverage.

"Do you know what happened to him?"

"When I returned the next day to his shop, I found the man immersed in his routine of evening prayer prostrations. I sat down on the couch near the door and waited. Upon completion, the man who turned to face me looked like a totally different person. He had slept through the night for the first time in a decade."

"That's amazing! What did he say?"

"He wanted to know how he could ever thank me. Now smiling and at peace with himself, he was then able to educate me that the Koran, from his perspective and understanding, was meant to provide residents a code of societal conduct, a method to coexist – given their own fractious history, going back eons."

"Wow! That's quite a story. It made an immediate difference to him in his life."

"I did suggest to him there was something he could do for me in return," my aunt continued with that troublemaker look on her face.

"What was that?" I asked curiously.

"He had shared with me that he hoped his daughter would be able to marry a good Pakistani man. I paused and then relayed that as I had sat with what had just transpired between us, I had been struck by the realization that the only reason I was on the other side of the world and having this conversation with him at all was because I'd had the benefit of a good education on multiple levels. So, then I asked him point-blank: what if the man she married was at some point unable to take care of her? If she had an education, she would be better equipped to support his grandchildren if something happened to her husband."

"How did he respond to that?" I asked, and before she had a chance to respond, I added, "And weren't you crossing the line just a little bit about not wanting anything in return?" My aunt laughed with me at my calling her to account.

"He couldn't help but agree with me. And yes, I did cross the line just a little bit." She paused for a moment and then added, "Although it was not a selfish request."

"It's one hell of a tale, Aunt Joni. I'm glad you were there for him. The timing in both your last examples does seem extraordinary under the circumstances. If we could all be so lucky!"

"Have you ever noticed we'll often attribute good things that happen to us that we don't otherwise understand to luck? Do you suppose, in the case of those two people, that we might factor in the clarity and intensity of their requests and their ability to find the right person to ask?"

"There you go again, giving me another opportunity to reexamine more elements of my obviously quirky thought process!"

"I've often heard it said that the universe provides. I've found it to be true, although, in some cases, it may not be what we think we want or need at that moment. It does appear to be possible for some of us to nearly immediately transcend these points in time when we've gotten seriously stuck. If it can happen with people worlds apart and different in every way, it can happen for society as a whole. If we're prepared to listen, then we, too, can share what we believe we know to be true and respectfully learn about ourselves and others in the process."

CHAPTER 25

It ALL Matters!

I was nearing the end of my visit with my aunt. We'd been cramming as much as possible into every last moment we had together. I was needed up north and would not be able to get back to see her for a while.

"So, what do you have to say for yourself about this first full leg of our passing the torch? Has it all made a dent?" my aunt asked me that evening, smiling.

"All I can say to all of this is wow! Aunt Joni, you've shared so much with me, and there's obviously so much more for me to learn and so little time in life. It clearly matters for each of us, for everyone around the world!"

"That's the spirit!"

"But I have to confess, I do have a couple of unresolved, only half-in-jest, nagging questions for you," I responded with one eyebrow raised.

"Oh?"

"Please don't take offense, but especially after hearing about your star-studded chart revelation, I have to ask: who the hell are you, anyway? I mean, really. That's number one. And secondly, how have you managed to figure all of this out? You just continue to blow my mind!" We looked at one another, and I shook my head at her, and then we both had to laugh.

"Well, those are fair questions. There was a time in my life I would have responded, 'I'm a flea on the elephant's back, that's who I am!' Then I would have asked you in return, 'How about you?'"

"Okay, fair enough."

"You now know there's always more to the story than meets the eye. It was not and is not my intent to keep you in the dark as to who I am. And yet I have to add that all of this, well, it stirs up an awful lot for me. I've asked for loads of help along the way. I know I've needed it, and I still do. It's true for all of us. Thankfully, we're all in this together. The forms and levels of my efforts to be responsive and of assistance continue to change, but I haven't stopped, cannot stop the work in progress that is my life."

"Okay, that says quite a bit, and…?" I gently prompted her for more.

"You've heard the expression that what you see is what you get?"

"Yeah."

"I'd say the truth is closer to what you see isn't always what you get."

"Huh?"

"Well, let's start with reality, or what we perceive to be reality, which, for most of us, is grounded in what we can visually see. Yet our physical eyes are not capable of seeing all that's there."

"What are you trying to say? I'm afraid I don't get it."

"Interestingly, our eyes are two dimensional in functionality. It's our mind that adds the element of distance, which provides us three-dimensionality in sight and allows us to distinguish form."

"Hmmph, I had no idea!"

"So, that's why the Zen master says that the room is the room, then the room is not the room, and then the room is the room again. What do you suppose he means?"

"You're asking me? I keep telling you I have no fricking idea!" I said, shaking my head and laughing. Thankfully, my aunt was able to continue without my mock frustration bowling her over.

"When our attention is firmly planted in consciousness and our eyes are open, the room is the room, yeah?"

"Okay, I'm with you so far."

"When our Eternal Observer is no longer in the conscious mind, but instead, say, following the path of the breath in and out of the lower diaphragm, and our physical eyes are open, eventually, we are able to experience the room without form, without three-dimensional reality."

I let out a very long "oh," followed by a "wow," as it finally dawned on me what she was really saying.

"For most, the first occurrence is followed by such shock that the attention cannot help but rush back up to conscious mind and vision, where it is used to residing, attempting to see that which can only be seen from someplace other than the conscious mind. To come full circle, that takes us instantaneously back to seeing the room as it is. It's one of many advancing signposts in this journey to watch for as your meditation practice strengthens."

I remember asking her about friends who'd confessed to trying to meditate but claimed they couldn't. "So, what are they missing, Aunt Joni?"

"As Palmer explained to us, there is a moment of frustration that can happen when one realizes several minutes later that their attention has returned to consciousness and they are back to thinking about something and no longer meditating."

"I can relate to that!" I laughed.

"It's critical not to shame oneself about it but simply let whatever the thought was go and return the attention to following the breath in and out of the lower diaphragm. It's a byproduct of consciousness as usual, really. The attention is used to dominating that space through a lifetime spent dwelling there, with consciousness and three-dimensional vision happily combined to cement reality as it is generally perceived."

"Okay, that's another huge bite for me to chew on," I responded, shaking my head in amazement. "And really helpful, thank you."

"That's why they call meditation a practice. It gets easier. It really does. The attention muscle gets stronger and stronger. And remember, as we begin to try to bring any part of 'the all that is' into words, we constrain that which is infinite, that which is unlimited."

"That explains quite a bit!" I offered in reply.

"It is difficult for anybody and everybody to attempt to communicate about it. It's even harder not to bring our conscious personal baggage with us to the proverbial table, much less deal with the myriad of thinking errors that inevitably arise from a solely consciousness-based focus of 'normal' life."

"You can say that again," I replied.

"Although communicating about spirituality and our respective psyches is mind-bogglingly difficult to attempt, it doesn't mean we can't try! There is a particular Zen expression that encapsulates this dilemma."

"What is it?"

"In the Zen way, one can only point," she responded without hesitation.

"I've heard that expression before, but I never really got it. Point at what?"

"Spirit comes from the void and returns to the void. It is non-matter. One can only point because to try to use words to describe it relies on consciousness, which limits our ability to truly understand our higher selves within eternity."

"That expression makes a whole lot more sense to me now," I confirmed.

"You'll know a blessing when you have surmounted normalcy, commencing an extraordinary journey while you're at it. When you get to that point, keep going!"

I had to laugh at that. She was right. By that point, I could truly see that the state of normal was really a matter of conscious perspective and it was all learned behavior. Who knew?

"Your grandmother Eloise, during her lifetime, stressed the importance of respecting others and their privacy. Similarly, Helen Palmer and many before her have stressed the importance of respecting the boundaries of someone else's psychic space. It is one thing for me to share my own psyche and experiences. For me to go plodding my way through someone else's psyche without invitation would be considered by many to be intrusive and disrespectful."

"Yeah, I get that."

"Maybe we've gotten spoiled by a personalized consciousness, thinking we can have a room of our own with a view," she suggested, being a bit flippant in the moment.

"Now, there's a hell of a perspective on life if I've ever heard one," I couldn't help but respond.

"Still, there's an awful lot of time being spent on the semantics of it all that still misses the boat that moves us further along the universal river."

"So, you're trying to tell me that words are useful pointers but they can also help get us sidetracked, yes?" I asked her.

"It's a true statement. In his memoir, Jung described being brought back to life and coming back into his body after having died as an extraordinarily painful experience. He conveyed that being brought back to form and consciousness was kind of like being squeezed into an overly tight shoebox in comparison to where he'd been in the interim. What an extraordinary gift to us in perspective."

"I'll second that," was all I could think of to say as I reflected on his in- and out-of-body experiences.

"I don't think I mentioned that it was Helen Palmer who encouraged us to practice mediation with our eyes open to remember that we're not sitting for personal enlightenment. The aim is to take all sentient creatures with us into enlightenment as we go."

"That helps bring the vision and conscious reality parts back into perspective again," I added, making the earlier connection.

"Good," she responded. "So, given the collective unconscious and the properties of morphic resonance, several cautions bubble up for me to share."

"What's that?" I asked, curious as to what was being stirred for my aunt.

"We are getting closer to reconnecting psychically on a broader scale than we've managed in a long time. The growing number of doctors and scientists separately trying to bridge the chasm between science and the infinite mind incarnated tells me the quickening process is farther along than I might have ever imagined."

"But that's kind of exciting, don't you think?"

"Yes, it is! However, if you take Jung and Rupert Sheldrake's contemporary findings together and then add in the brutalities of the last couple of thousand years, it does suggest there's a severely traumatized layer of the collective unconscious memory of 'power over' abuses."

"Oh," I responded cautiously, "I didn't think about that!"

"When you start cracking open collective 'normal' reality to open up to all that is, there's an awful lot of vulnerable people who, without tools, direction, or preparation, could potentially be traumatized by their experiences. It's no coincidence that people don't want to come out of their clamshells – in many respects, it hasn't truly been safe to do so for a long time."

"So, what does all of this mean?"

"In short, it amounts to a substantial part of our collective unconscious that isn't participating in a healthy balance of it all. The longer we maintain these gross imbalances in the psychic realms, the harder it will be to move the attention, which becomes further and further stuck in the mud, unable to move to new assemblage points."

"Okay, that helps, and it's starting to make some sense."

"I hope for a time when humans will recognize that each of our individualized set of biases in perspective is ultimately hindering our ability to find common ground."

"Wouldn't that be awesome?" I could see the enormous potential, but my inner skeptic was trained to start doubting at the slightest hint of anything out of the ordinary.

"There is such a place of common ground, you now know. There is a place we can all go, essentially free of conscious perspective, that we can share together. From my personal experience, I would offer that it is a space truly vital for individual and community health and holds the key to greater work together as one people of this planet. Beautifully, it does not supplant anyone's religion, creed, or color."

"I like the sound of that," I responded.

"We get there by starting with the limitations of our personal biases and our biases toward history. It's clear from the experience we've shared that history takes on new forms of relevance for us when it is made personal."

"You can say that again."

"When I learned that four out of five of us employ vision as the primary modality of our senses, it clicked for me. If we could each revisit our familial histories, experience the lives of our ancestors with all of the cultural norms and idiosyncrasies of their eras, and, ideally for most of us, if we were able to do that visually or, say, through virtual reality, my guess is we'd increase the efficacy of our educational trajectories by warp-speed factors."

"That was quite a mouthful you just put out there, not to mention one hell of an idea, but why not? It could really make a difference."

"From there, it's an easy jump to see that when we're truly driven to find common ground, we'll go to the space we all have within us, our true law nature, to meet and be as one."

"I really appreciate your willingness to tackle all my questions, Aunt Joni. I also want you to hear that I very much appreciate your patience with me. It's all making a difference."

"I'm overjoyed to hear it! We have so much ground yet to cover, you and me, and so many tales still to share," my aunt said as her voice trailed off into the night.

"Dad told me that you've led an epic life," I couldn't help interjecting. "I can't wait to hear your tales."

"Oh, my life is one big unexplainable event, all right!" She chuckled, turned her face and palms up to the heavens, and then added sarcastically, "Thankfully, he doesn't know the half of it! How about we save those years in between for the third volume, eh?"

"So, Grandma Eloise's family is the second volume?"

"That will be next! You think the Whitmores have some tales? These Winn tales are every bit as unbelievable and then some! And we'll pick up with a number of the threads we've begun in this one."

I beamed back my understanding. Once again, there was nothing to do but wait. I had a hard time imagining how a group of stories could be more unbelievable than what she'd already shared, yet I knew her well enough now to know she was trying to prepare me for more to come. My brother had begun to drop hints to me on the side as to what they were uncovering in their research. There was more un-fucking-believable history that would shed even more light on why we'd all gotten so damn stuck. Yet I could see she was tiring. I knew her much, much better now.

"Some think big; some think small. It all matters," my aunt continued. "It takes all those indecipherably small steps to make or do something great. Once done, we see the end result and can only marvel at it. Then human nature begs us to ask the question that keeps us striving forward. How did you do it?" Aunt Joni asked rhetorically.

"How did you do it, aunt Joni?" I asked her directly.

"And thus begins the process anew – of learning from one another over time and through space. How did you do it?" she repeated. "Do you have any idea how often I've been asked that question?"

"Do you have any idea how often I've asked you that question?"

We broke into laughter that carried across the pond. We laughed until we nearly cried.

When we caught our breath and stillness returned, my aunt turned her head to look at me and said very quietly, "I haven't forgotten any of your questions, my dear one. While you were getting your things together, I ran across something I wrote about myself several years ago that might answer some of them. I'll share it with you here in a minute if you like."

"That'd be great! As it is, you're still leaving me with a lot to get my head around," I replied truthfully.

"Hopefully, we'll have a chance to continue all of this soon. Until then, I've left you with the key. Don't forget! It's in your attention. When you're ready, use it to open the door. Soon enough, it'll be your turn to pass the torch!"

"Thank you, Aunt Joni, and please proceed!"

CHAPTER 26

Explain Your Self: In One Moment

ONE TWO ONE ONE
MOMENT
I AM ALL HERE NOW
THANKFUL THIS MOMENT
ALL I AM, ALL I EVER AM
ALL I WILL, ALL I AM
THIS MOMENT
ONE TWO ONE ONE

I am a child of intention: a doctor's order for a long-scrambled egg fertilized by everyone under the sun. My brother before me rests in peace. The last of five intended children, he shares eight precious hours before returning home; his heart, his rhythm, unable to stay.

Born a blazing question I ask my Self: who am I? Is it possible to know before birth, choosing when to arrive? Perspective is everything and nothing, upside down, backward. As you now know, dyslexia is one of many gifts in store for me to explore.

In this one moment, judgment suspended, in one moment.

My parents set me loose alone. Barefoot, I walk from north to south the shoreline of the Oregon coast as a young child, feeling the ocean lap my feet, looking to the sun warming my face as it sets on the western horizon, dawning to the east.

A universal hammer arrives to strike me, but I am too young to recognize it, and I hold no fear. Out of nowhere, I hear a song in my mind: FREE WHAT YOU WANT TO BE, YOU AND ME, FOR ETERNITY, WE'RE FREE, AS FAR AS LIFE CAN SEE NOW. I wonder in awe where the song came from.

The hammer continues to increase in frequency. I search the world to answer my Self. Could something as complex as mind be without an updated operating manual? I wonder my Self. I ask many to answer for me and receive pointers back to myself in real time, in conscious reality.

Did I mention I come from a long line of pie makers that love to puzzle? You can't miss this one. One big circle, and you can slice it and dice it any way you want to get to the center – it doesn't matter. I remember wizard pi, the constant that is and is not a constant. Being irrational, its decimal representation never ends and, more importantly, never settles into a permanent repeating pattern.

So, here is my ultimate baker's challenge, and somewhere along the way, I set my Self to this recipe. Could I create one whole pie that would truly matter? Jung shared the collective unconscious recipe and beyond when he passed in 1961; my mother and father, with all my relations, had the rest of the ingredients, with the intent to fill the prescription ASAP. Add morphic resonance to me and shake until stirred. Then, like yeast to bread, time causes me to grow and, like a wonderful wine, allows me to age. And voilà!

I AM NOW,
No longer a question
Whether BE or not,
I AM
Along alone with ALL for this festival ride to
Enjoy a cosmic feast!

You ask me to speak plainly. Explain yourself!

I shattered the glass ceiling for my Self, answering that question I was born to answer myself. I am, and we each are, living proof of morphic resonance. The proof is everywhere, right and left, inside out, all at once as one!

That Sunday morning in August of 2014, I was awake when the 6.0 earthquake hit. I knew then I would not be going back to sleep. I found Krishnamurti's *Freedom from the Known* waiting for me, and I devoured it ravenously like a meal I hadn't eaten in eons. I came to the story of the monks and the woman at the river and recognized it from memory. I'd read *Freedom from the Known* thirty years ago, while I was still in California, and then had let it all go to Alaska. Now I am full circle. I spent the rest of the day in another world, as quiet as possible.

I somehow knew to synchronize my birth month and day, and my birth hour and minute, on coming into consciousness in this physical lifetime.

My son, a double physics and math honors graduate, assured me there was plenty of probability within the infinite universe to have nailed this one birth date and time together on the head coming in – no big deal from his perspective. But what's the probability a bunch of us are coming in this same way? We didn't have to look far to discover an array of synchronized miracles already here.

Federal law at the time of my congressional campaign didn't give a hoot about personal privacy. I've found my birth date all over the internet for everyone to know, so no big deal if I share it here now. I was born on December 11, 1961. What isn't known is that I was born on 12-11 at 12:11 am.

I spent years sitting with this one. How could I have known to give my Self such a synchronistic pointer?

If morphic resonance is truly reflective of our ability to learn from one another across space and time, there ought to be others, as we immediately discovered. Is this more evidence of consilience emerging?

Thirty years ago, I was still trying to figure out how I could be having intuitive, synchronistic experiences with machines like cars and mainframe computers without intent to do so! Then, Saturday, August 23, that long-sought answer was delivered to my psychic mailbox. I now know that my mind, with the ability to extend beyond the constraints of space and time, only needed to look forward into the future to find my birthdate all over the internet, strung out there in space and time for everyone to see.

With Jung's help guiding another cosmic giggle, a synchronicity even a dyslexic would recognize could be formed for me to re-member myself – if I were to intend to arrive at a precise moment that mirrored itself! Morphic resonance emanating within our collective unconscious could produce and explain both this result and revelation to put Humpty Dumpty back together again.

I am jumping for joy! To all my relations, thank you, one and all in this moment!

Be, here, now, then, gives new meaning to Self, in all dimensions!
1 2 1 1 1 2 1 1

CHAPTER 27

The Unnamed One:
UNO

I directed the focus of my attention back to the group of family and friends in front of me.

"So, now you know how I got dragged into all of this wonderful stuff," I said to laughter from the group. "The potential and realization of peace and so much more is within us all. We each hold the key to its longer-term exercise, personally, culturally, and throughout societies near and far. Where and when does the madness end? It ends when each of us is united in humanity with the knowledge and wisdom to accountably exercise power over our individual little ego-selves around the world. We can, we must, and we will overcome ourselves!"

I watched eyes and smiles light up and heard more wonderful expressions of laughter and delight from the group.

"Helen Palmer schooled Aunt Joni and classes full of students with the capacity of all of her being, introducing them to intuition, the lifelong companionship of meditation, guided dreaming, and the work to be done on multiple levels along the way. I have to acknowledge that it took my aunt all of her patience to get through this with me," I admitted to more laughter and heads nodding in understanding.

"Critically, Helen taught them that to successfully move one's attention, one must have the intent to move it. Then one must have the will to keep it in the new position. That was also huge for me to digest at the time. Now we can each know and realize in our own time that the intent to move and the will to maintain our attention in new positions are celestial keys to life, the universe, and everything."

I paused for just a moment.

"Aunt Joni is now reminding me with all of her being of the importance in this moment of the extraordinary analogy provided by Canadian geese. When flying in formation as a group, they increase their total flight capacity by sixty to seventy percent!"

The sounds of human exclamations from around the room filled my ears with joy.

"Hearing that fact was one of my own breakthrough moments of understanding and self-realization. It brought everything I'd learned from her about our united potentiality into focus. Prior to that point, I was never really able to figure out how my aunt survived our family, much less accomplished so much in her lifetime. All these years later, I know for myself, without a doubt."

I looked into the eyes of every person around the room before I finished my train of thought.

"You don't need me to tell you that the universe awaits us all. It is a point in time and space we can all embrace in the moment.

Until then, I'll offer you one more circle around for a toast to truth, which appears, at least for now, to still be stranger to us than fiction."

"May you see the light, be the light, and pass the torch!"

The End

Acknowledgments

I give thanks to my classmate Gretchen Wendell, nearly forty years ago, for bringing to my attention *The Timetables of History,* published in 1946 by Bernard Grun. I'm appreciative of the kindness of the AMES Plantation staff, for sharing their records and graciously educating me about my ancestors Burwell & Amanda Whitmore, in Grand Junction, Tennessee.

I credit the Washington Post, January 24, 2015, and the Federal Reserve, in my use of wealth and race data from the FRSB *Survey of Consumer Finances,* reflecting the wealth gap widening from rising home values, financial and other assets. In 1993, white families held 4.6 times the wealth of black families. By 2013, white families held seven times the wealth of black families.

I am grateful to the Pew Charitable Trust, for 2015 religious data from 'The Changing Global Religious Landscape'. Of the estimated 7.3 billion people on the planet at that time:

1.1 Billion	16%	Religiously Unaffiliated
1.8 Billion	24%	Muslim
2.3 Billion	31%	Christian
1.1 Billion	15%	Hindu
.5 Billion	7%	Buddhist
.51 Billion	7%	Other*

*Includes: Folk Religions .4 Billion, Judaism .01 Billion, all other .1 Billion.

I want to credit CNN for the February 5, 2012 coverage of Virginia Historical Society CEO/President Paul Levengood, providing insight on where "slavery began in the American colonies in 1619." I'll credit Wikipedia for information on societies, archives and websites about Virginia, and specific data on Dinwiddie County. Virginia had the largest free population of blacks, with an 8/1 ratio of enslaved to free black people. In the town of Petersburg, Dinwiddie County, in 1830, there were 3,440 whites, 2,850 enslaved blacks, and 2,032 free black people.

I will credit two websites for Arkansas history: encylopediaofarkansas.net as well as historicalarkansas.org/collections-and-research/Arkansas-history-timeline-1819-1861. The sites noted the 1822 Indian Peace Treaty with the Osage & Cherokee Tribes, and Arkansas as furthest western frontier of the U.S. From 1820 to 1830, the bulk of American Indians there were moved to Oklahoma, and the Final Indian Treaty with the Cherokee Nation was concluded. 'Freed' of all tribal property, these now public lands in the territory were sold into private hands through federal offices. The area west of Arkansas was established as the repository for the Indian Nations. Arkansas was subsequently brought into the Union in 1836.

I am indebted to Ms. Jada Aitchison, Acquisitions & Reference Librarian, for her assistance navigating the UALR/Pulaski County Law Library. They ask that the library and these cases regarding Richard August and Junius Brown Whitmore are noted accordingly:

1. Arkansas Supreme Court Briefs and Records, Series II, Criminal, Box 540, Folder 5284, *Whitmore v. Tatum*, 54 Ark. 457 (1891), UALR/Pulaski County Law Library, Special Collections.

2. Arkansas Supreme Court Briefs and Records, Series I, Criminal, Box 183, Folder 3389, *Mock v. Pleasants*, 34 Ark. 63 (1879), UALR/Pulaski County Law Library, Special Collections.

I read through many sites and volumes before I confirmed the Whitmore family legend to be true. *The Domesday Book of 1085* provided the clearest evidence. These sites also enhanced my understanding: normandythenandnow.com, Thehistoryofengland. co.uk, Englishmonarchs.co.uk, Normanconnections.com, houseofnames.com, and History.com. The lineage questions relating to kings, queens, and dukes of Normandy and England were clarified by these sites: historic_uk.com, wikipedia.org, and ffish.com. I must also acknowledge the assistance of The Anglo-Saxon Chronicle, published by Benjamin Thorpe, Royal Academy of Science, 1861, and https//archive.org/stream/ anglosaxonchroni02thoruoft/anglosaxonchroni02thoruoft_djvu. txt. I found further information about the Whitmore family at: dwhitmore.thewhitmorefamily.com/whitstaf.thm. It was helpful to learn about Sir George & Sir John of the New Haven Colony in 1638 from https://archive.org/stream/Whitmoregenealog01purd/ Whitmoregeneal01purd-djvu.text.

In addition to all my relations, I must acknowledge and humbly thank my advisors, readers, listeners, researchers, graphic artists, photographers, scanners, reviewers, and editors from beginning to end, including Reverend Paula Whitmore, whose initial findings generously shared were critical for the family at large to understand; Guy Goode, who read through numerous drafts over a decade; along with involvement and support from Dani Tanzella, Thomas Whitmore, Scott Taylor, Valerie Bettencourt, Tim Mooney, Rachel Edler, Patrick Whitmore, John Bajowski, Jackie Davis, Michael Whitmore, Christina Park, Holly Dotson, Tyler Holt, Nelson and Susan Weinberg, Kathryne Ann Kinsey, Alison Barrows Ronn, Julie Trelstad, Julie-Ink, and their entire crew. Many thanks to Peter and Carolyn Whitmore Baldwin and Rupert Sheldrake, for their tireless efforts toward the public good, along with their insightful and helpful correspondence.

Above and beyond thanks to our webmaster, Scott Taylor, Sharestragies.com. Enjoy our website, TorchTimeTales.org, for additional features, productions and credits. Watch our videos on YouTube, with hats off to Robert Parish, WriteFieldFeatures. My thanks to Scott Taylor for construction and maintenance of our Facebook page, and Robert Parish, for administration assistance.

I would like to offer immense gratitude to the combined efforts of Kosei/Weatherhill Publishing for printing *The Threefold Lotus Sutra* in English in 1975, which helped me save my life. I owe significant debts of gratitude: to producer Robert Parish, whose tireless efforts continue to set the standard for all involved, and to Bergitta Trelstad, who assumes responsibility as successor trustee to my perpetual literary trust, when my own time comes. For those I have overlooked, the responsibility and regret, rests with the author.

Lastly, with a nod to the gifts of dyslexia, and in no way least of all these acknowledgments, I pay tribute to both literary hallmarks that were set to work in my mind's eye some fifty years ago: *Seven Arrows*, by Hyemeyohsts Storm, in 1972; and *Roots*, the book and television series, by Alex Haley in 1976-1977.

CPSIA information can be obtained
at www.ICGtesting.com
Printed in the USA
LVHW081911220722
723880LV00012B/343